Home Office

VOLATILE SUBSTANCE ABUSE

A Report by the
Advisory Council on the Misuse of Drugs

LONDON: HMSO

ISBN 0 11 341141 3

CONTENTS

LIST OF APPENDICES

ADVISORY COUNCIL ON THE MISUSE OF DRUGS

Members

Professor D Grahame-Smith, CBE Chairman
Mrs J Barlow
Mr R Bartle
Dr W Clee
Mr D Coleman
Dr M Donmall
Dr A Duxbury
Professor G Edwards, CBE
Mrs J Faugier
Dr J Greenwood
Ms K Hager
Mr P Hayes
Mr K Hellawell
Ms L Hewitt
Mr M Hindson
Professor R Jones
Ms R Joyce
Mr J Kay
Dr M Keen, OBE
Dr D Kennedy
Professor M Lader
Mr A Massam
Mr M Narayn Singh
Professor W Ollis
Mr K Patel
Dr D Patterson
Mr A Ramsay
Dr S Ruben
Viscountess Runciman, OBE
Mr I Sherwood
Professor G Stimson
Professor J Strang
Dr D Temple
Mr D Turner
Mr E Unsworth
Mr P Walker
Dr T Waller

PREFACE

Volatile substance abuse (VSA) is a phenomenon which has existed in one form or another since the turn of the century. Only in the past 20 years or so has increasingly widespread abuse become a cause for concern. It is this concern which has led us to write this report. We would not wish to suggest that a crisis point has been reached. Rather we believe that VSA is a continuing, unpredictable and easily ignored issue, needing and deserving more attention.

In some areas up to 10% of young people have inhaled volatile substances. This is very worrying since typical users are of an age (11 to 17) when they should be maximising the opportunities available to them rather than attracting the problems which VSA can bring. The wide range of substances which are inhaled are readily available and dangerous and, in extreme cases, immediate death results. The numbers of fatalities in the United Kingdom are not insignificant (averaging over 100 in each of recent years). For some age groups this exceeds the number of deaths from leukaemia, pneumonia and drowning put together. Up to 40% of deaths occur on the first occasion of abuse. While abusers may do damage to themselves it is not only they who suffer. Once the abuse becomes evident it can bring a sense of fright and confusion to parents. And it can also have adverse effects on other families through fear of their children becoming involved, while the wider community may be worried about such consequences as unruly public behaviour. In short, VSA is a cause of widespread problems which must not be ignored.

A report of this kind cannot be all inclusive but our hope is that you, in whatever capacity, will read it and draw on it for those matters which are relevant to you. In this way VSA as a concern should stay high on the local and national agenda and, as a result, some lives will be saved.

SUMMARY AND RECOMMENDATIONS

PREFACE

The purpose of this report is to heighten awareness of volatile substance abuse (VSA) as a multi-faceted and widespread social problem, and stimulate a programme of action. **VSA should be accorded greater salience on community agendas and professional concerns.** Through the integrated community responses which are now proposed, lives can be saved.

CHAPTER 1. BACKGROUND AND CONTEXT

1 The present report builds on, and is linked to, ACMD's report on Drug Education in Schools. Many of the issues raised by VSA are common to other types of drug misuse. This problem does, however, have some sufficiently distinct features such as the pervasive availability of the substances, early onset of use, and risk of sudden death even on first experiment, to persuade us that **VSA today constitutes a topic worthy of focused attention in its own right.** (1.4)

2 VSA can be defined as "deliberate inhalation of a volatile substance to achieve a change in mental state". (1.5)

3 Although problems with VSA include morbidity as well as mortality, the prevention of unnecessary and tragic deaths must be a prime social concern. In 1990, 151 young people died as a consequence of this behaviour. VSA accounts for an eighth of the total deaths among boys in the 11-17 years age group, and for this age group exceeds combined deaths from leukaemia, drowning and pneumonia. (1.9)

4 The Intoxicating Substances Supply Act of 1985 makes it an offence in the UK (other than Scotland), for anyone to sell a substance (other than a controlled drug) to a person aged under 18, knowing that "the substance or its fumes are likely to be inhaled . . . for the purpose of causing intoxication". The relevance of certain other legislation is considered. **We do not believe that any further enactments would at present be helpful in controlling VSA.** (1.14 – 1.28)

CHAPTER 2. CAUSES, PREVALENCE AND PATTERNS

5 The aim of this chapter is to establish as best possible what is known about the causes of VSA, and its prevalence, and patterns of use. It is possible to give a useful outline, but the gaps in information are large and must be admitted. **The available research amply demonstrates that VSA is a rather common but complex, socially embedded problem, affecting many different young people for different reasons and in varying degrees. Only that vision of complexity will serve society well when designing responses.** (2.1 – 2.5)

6 There is no single reason for young people becoming involved in VSA. The problem is likely to arise from interaction of social, family, and psychological factors. Personal disadvantage or family problems may often be part of this background, but VSA is not confined to any one social group. (2.6 – 2.13)

7 Patterns of use exist in a continuum ranging through experimentation, which is common, controlled or episodic use, which is not uncommon, and chronic use, which is less common. VSA is mainly a group activity. Little is known about the relationship between VSA and other types of drug misuse, either cross-sectionally or longitudinally. (2.14 – 2.18)

8 Techniques of use include pouring a substance into a plastic bag, direct inhalation from containers, or spraying directly into the mouth. All these modes of use are dangerous. (2.16)

9 Prevalence of VSA varies geographically, and can fluctuate rapidly over time. An "average" statement on prevalence is therefore of limited meaning, but it would not be unusual to find that a small percentage of 8-10 years olds have experimented, while among teenagers 5-10% may have engaged in VSA at some time, with a higher figure in some areas. (2.19 – 2.30)

10 Mortality rates from VSA have since 1971 been reported annually by a group at St George's Hospital, London. The total number of VSA deaths recorded from 1971-1992 was 1317, but this figure is likely to be an underestimate. The peak age for VSA deaths is 14-18, and in all age groups male mortality significantly exceeds female. (2.31 – 2.41)

11 VSA is a problem in many other countries beside the UK, including the USA, Japan and parts of the developing world, but it appears at present to be relatively uncommon (or unrecognised) in continental Europe. (2.42 – 2.45)

12 A strengthened and more informed response to VSA will require improved understanding of causes, patterns and prevalence. We recommend that the current relative neglect of social and epidemiological research on this topic should be remedied and hope that the Department of Health will take the lead in stimulating and co-ordinating a research initiative. Mortality data provide a valuable epidemiological indicator, and support for the St George's team should be continued. There would be benefit if coroners were to note any connection with VSA in the additional comments which are given by them in Part IV of notification forms. (2.34)

CHAPTER 3. TOXICOLOGY

13 An informed community and professional awareness of the problems set by VSA must include an understanding that the substances which are misused are toxic chemicals which are at the same time mind-acting drugs. (3.1)

14 The range of volatile substances capable of misuse is immensely wide, but for the most part involves the three chemical groupings of aliphatic hydrocarbons (eg butane), aromatic hydrocarbons (principally toluene), and halogenated carbons of a type common until recently in aerosol propellants.

Commercial products often contain a mix of solvents. Unlike a tablet or a half pint of beer, solvent use is by its nature a gamble with an uncertain quantity of intake, and with a narrow margin between wanted and disastrous effects. (3.4 - 3.7)

15 The range of commercially available products in which these abusable chemicals are to be found is also immensely extensive, and includes adhesives, aerosols, anaesthetics, commercial dry cleaning and degreasing products, fire extinguishers, fuel gases, nail varnish remover, paint thinners or strippers, and typewriter correction fluids. (3.6)

16 VSA is for the most part best seen as drug abuse rather than drug dependence, but a small minority of users may contract a compulsive, long term habit. (3.11)

17 VSA is unique among drug problems because sudden death is the most common complication bringing the user to notice. Causes of death include direct toxic effects, and indirect causes such as falls or drowning when intoxicated, inhalation of vomit, or fire or explosion. (3.13)

18 Chronic damage to body tissues can result from repeated or prolonged exposure to volatile substances. The dangers should not be exaggerated, but there is research to suggest that damage can occur to the brain, the optic nerve, the inner ear, muscles, peripheral nerves, liver, kidneys, lung and bone marrow. (3.14 – 3.15)

19 The conclusion to be drawn from a review of the substances involved in VSA must be that the problem cannot be dealt with by eliminating the supply of the abusable drugs. The substances which give rise to VSA are to be found in every home and workplace. The worrying and difficult paradox which arises is that we are dealing here with abusable, toxic, and potentially lethal drugs, which are at the same time the constituents of household and industrial products of enormously wide application and utility, and which will for the most part be safely used. In shaping policy, a sense of balance must be retained.

20 There needs to be greater awareness of the true, worrying facts about danger. No VSA is without risk.

CHAPTER 4. PREVENTION

21 Prevention strategies must be designed both in the light of an awareness of the personal and social background to VSA (chapter 2), and the toxicological facts and a knowledge of the types of product which are involved (chapter 3). **Prevention must thus be both person and community focused, and product focused.**

22 The fundamental and consistent message which we advocate for all health statements on this topic made to young people as individuals or to wider target audiences, is the unambiguous – "VSA is too dangerous, don't do it". Given the mortality risks which attach to this form of drug misuse this message is accurate, and it should be repeated squarely and without proviso or confusion. We are not here advocating scare tactics, but the simple, supportable, repeated statement of the plain truth. Abusing volatile substances is like playing Russian roulette. (4.2 – 4.3)

23 With some committed users no advice is likely to bring immediate cessation. Without accidentally conveying the misleading and dangerous message that any form of VSA can be safe, it is legitimate with such users to suggest strategies which may reduce danger. For instance, it may be appropriate to counsel against use in circumstances which carry particularly strong risk of accidental fatal drowning, or fire or explosion. There is no contradiction between the general message "Don't do it, it's too dangerous", and in special and individual circumstances working for intermediate goals and avoidance of worse consequences. (4.6)

24 Between those who are receptive to the general "VSA is too dangerous, don't do it" message and the committed abuser there will be a wide range of young people with varying knowledge and life-skills. **It follows that**

education on VSA needs tailoring to the particular circumstances of those in the educational group. The general "VSA is too dangerous, don't do it" message should not be used heedlessly or as a slogan but as the invariable basis of any discussions which explore VSA and how to avoid its more dangerous forms. The aim should be to help young people make healthy, informed decisions. (4.6)

25 We attach great importance to demand reduction. **School based education on VSA should be integrated with drug education and teach decision making and life skills within the model previously proposed in the ACMD report on drug education in schools.** The provision of information for parents is also very important, and we commend the Department of Health leaflet on "Drugs and Solvents – you and your child". (4.15 – 4.18)

26 Strategies for controlling supply and access can offer multiple small gains and will be usefully complementary to the demand reduction approaches which we have outlined above. **Parents and carers should take sensible safeguards in the home, and potentially abusable substances should be responsibly handled wherever they are used. Trade associations have a responsibility in getting a VSA prevention message to retailers.** (4.26 and 4.31)

27 A variety of approaches to product design and modification can help to make potentially abusable substances less easy to administer or less attractive. The Montreal Convention and subsequent European Community negotiations will decrease or ban the use of ozone depleting substances in aerosol systems, and we urge manufacturers to consider the abuse potential of any substitute chemicals. **We are particularly worried about the sale of cigarette lighter refills in sizes which give ready access to dangerous amounts of butane. We recommend that the size of such refills should be limited to 25 ml.** (4.33 – 4.36)

28 On product labelling, we firstly recommend that wholesalers should include on their packaging a message to identify products which are liable to abuse, and hence alert shopkeepers to risk. Secondly, we recommend that parents should be provided with warnings about products liable to abuse with labels of appropriate size and clarity. Such labelling can only be

introduced on a voluntary basis. (4.37 – 4.43)

29 Our recommendations for product modification and labelling will require support from industry. **We strongly recommended the establishment of an industry-led forum, perhaps with representatives from Re-Solv and others, to share ideas and experience and secure relevant action. This initiative should be stimulated by Government.** (4.44)

30 Our recommendations in this chapter cover a very wide range of matters. **Much of what we say is based on our assessment that there is a need to heighten public awareness of VSA in order that its prevention receives the attention which it deserves.** (4.45 – 4.47)

CHAPTER 5. STRENGTHENING COMMUNITY-BASED HELP FOR VOLATILE SUBSTANCE MISUSERS AND THEIR FAMILIES

31 **A strategy to provide strengthened help for volatile substance misusers and their families must be developed within a framework which builds on existing and largely generic community resources, and which recognises that the pattern of local responses to local problems must be locally determined. We identify the main features which characterise such a framework.** (5.1 and 5.4)

32 Help for the individual who is misusing volatile substances will involve choices between a series of interventions of graded intensity, rather than any one master-stroke. **The basis for all types of help given to the volatile substance misuser must though be simple and informed advice, and the ability to enter into sympathetic dialogue.** Far from dismissing this level of response as trivial or obvious, we believe that it is this kind of community response to VSA which needs in particular to be strengthened – whether from professionals, parents or friends, or, for instance, the caretaker in the block of flats where the misuser might live. (5.6 – 5.10)

33 When more intensive help is needed this too must be flexible and graded rather than any one package. Within a given community there should be a variety of skills and experience within statutory and non-statutory organisations which can contribute to such work. Rarely, residential help may be needed. (5.11 – 5.15)

34 A flexible range of support and assistance will also be needed for families. (5.16 5.17)

CHAPTER 6. TRAINING

35 Our analysis of the training problem set by VSA and of how training needs should be met are based on the 1990 ACMD Training report, and the 1993 report on Drug Education in Schools. (6.1)

36 Educationalists will firstly require relevant training relating to their strictly education role. As with drug education, so with VSA we see training as enhancing the teacher's capacity to convey knowledge, strengthen decision-making skills, change attitudes and behaviour in healthy directions, and promote responsible citizenship. (6.4)

37 We reiterate the need for a strong organisational base for drug education in schools, within which initial and in-service training on VSA can be provided for teachers. (6.2 – 6.7)

38 Besides training on directly educational issues, teachers should secondly be given training on pastoral issues which can occur with VSA, again within the context of recommendations made within previous reports. (6.8)

39 The training needs on VSA for many other professions besides teachers must also be met, including those of nurses, doctors, social workers, youth and community workers, the police, pharmacists and the probation service. We recommend that each of these professions should examine the adequacy of current training on VSA, and validating bodies should determine the basic details of knowledge on VSA appropriate to

their professions. We recommend that with in-service and multidisciplinary training on drug issues, VSA should be given adequate coverage. Purchasers when setting relevant contracts should specify the degree of training on VSA which is required, and providers should ensure that it is given. (6.9 – 6.21)

40 We believe that it is unfortunate that the substance abuse option of the level 3 Care National and Scottish Vocation Qualifications (N/SVQ) contains no reference to VSA and that there is no consideration yet being given within the developing N/SVQ systems to developing the competency of youth and community workers in relation to drug and volatile substance misusers. **We recommend that the relevant lead bodies give these issues their urgent attention.** (6.17)

41 In our previous training report we argued for a new national training development agency. This development has not taken place. There is still a gap in leadership of training at a national level and a need to identify and promote good practice in training. **We recommend that the Department of Health should consider how it can support the drugs field in drawing up proposals for a co-ordinated response to the training needs of both specialists and non-specialists on VSA, in what ever capacity and however infrequently they may need to address the issue of VSA.** (6.22)

CHAPTER 7. PLANNING THE RESPONSE TO VSA

42 **We recommend that an effective mechanism for planning the overall response to VSA should be established throughout the country at local level.** Without such a mechanism the problem of VSA will too easily drop from sight, and our recommendations on prevention (chapter 4), treatment (chapter 5), and training (chapter 6) would remain as unimplemented good intentions. (7.1 – 7.2)

43 **The person who is to take lead co-ordinating responsibility for response to VSA and the office or organisation within which they are to be**

located must be for local decision, but it is vital that a named person is identified, and their identity widely known in their community. We recommend that the Director of Public Health should be responsible for ensuring that a suitable co-ordinator is identified. (7.3 – 7.4)

44 Local responses to VSA should not be designed blind to the facts, and **we recommend that plans for addressing VSA in each locality should be based on some information rather than none at all. Enquiry rather than formal research may be sufficient usefully to map the field.** (7.9)

45 We recommend that the local co-ordinator should identify current resources for response to VSA and related gaps in provision, establish a co-ordinating group, and disseminate information. The emphasis will be on identifying and supporting multiple, generic, community based capacities to deal with VSA, rather than the co-ordinator becoming the one-person referral point. (7.10)

46 Local responses to VSA should be designed in liaison with those concerned with wider substance misuse problems. The degree of identity or separation between the planning of responses to VSA and these other problems must, however, again be a matter decided locally. Some groups or families may at times be happier if the response to VSA is not too closely affiliated with other drug services. We caution against the danger of VSA being sidelined or lost within planning dominated by concerns for other substances. (7.10 - 7.11)

47 To ensure that progress is made in strengthening the local response to VSA, **we recommend that targets in the form of "action points" should be set at community level.** (7.13)

48 Our larger emphasis is on enhancing the extent, integration and efficacy of local action on VSA, and on that basis a summed country-wide strengthening of responses to VSA can be expected. For the success of this community-based approach, **a measure of enhanced national support will, however, be needed. This is likely in particular to entail means for**

exchanging experience in good practice, and central provision of training opportunities and material. We recommend that the lead should be taken by the Health Departments, and that the Departments should consider how local action can best be promoted. (7.15 – 7.16)

49 The most obvious and testing outcome indicators for the proposals made in this report and the organisational strategies outlined in this chapter would be a reduction in VSA deaths and the prevalence of VSA. **We have concluded that, while it would be desirable to have national targets, the nature of the mortality data and the absence of prevalence data make the setting of meaningful national targets impractical. However, we suggest that periodic surveys, carried out by the Department of Health, of local responses to VSA might provide data useful in helping to ascertain whether coverage is adequate and in planning future responses.** (7.17 – 7.19)

CHAPTER 1

BACKGROUND AND CONTEXT

Introduction

1.1 The Advisory Council on the Misuse of Drugs (ACMD) was set up by the Misuse of Drugs Act 1971 with the duty to keep under review the problems of drug misuse and to advise Ministers on ways of dealing with them. This report on volatile substance abuse (VSA) has been prepared by a Working Group of the Council, convened in 1991 to examine prevention issues, and has been endorsed by full Council. A list of members of the Working Group, including co-opted members and officials, is at appendix A.

Background

1.2 The Working Group's initial terms of reference were:

> "To consider and advise, in the light of the Advisory Council's report on Prevention (published in 1984) [1], on preventive measures to reduce the risk of an individual engaging in drug misuse or to reduce the harm associated with drug misuse."

1.3 The Prevention Working Group therefore has a remit to look at all aspects of drug prevention work in the UK. The field of prevention is so large, however, that the Group decided it would be impractical to aim towards producing another general report, especially as the principles outlined in its 1984 report were largely still valid. Instead, it decided it would consider specific topics in more detail.

1.4 Since 1984 trends in drug misuse appear to have been steadily rising. Any strategy that aims to tackle the various problems of drug misuse must make preventive education among young people a key part of the strategy. For our first area of study we therefore chose drug education in schools [(2)]. In the course of preparing our report we examined the available data on drug misuse among school-age children and VSA stood out as one of the most common problems and one which generally affected children younger than those involved in other forms of drug misuse. We therefore decided as our second area of work to carry out a study specifically on the topic of volatile substance abuse. The question might then be asked whether it is proper for the ACMD, which was set up to look into drug misuse, to take VSA within its remit. We believe it is. VSA, while distinct in several ways from conventional drug misuse, is entered into for much the same reasons. It affects the senses and, as with drug misuse, can cause harm to the individual directly or indirectly. It tends to attract younger misusers and the means are more readily available. For all these reasons we believe it merits consideration by this group, and as a subject taken on its own, but certainly considered within the broader context.

Definitions and context

1.5 VSA has been defined as "deliberate inhalation of a volatile substance to achieve a change in mental state". It is more commonly described as "glue-sniffing" or solvent abuse but in fact the range of substances misused is very wide and includes substances which are not solvents or glue. For this reason we have decided to use the wider term volatile substance abuse or VSA throughout this report. We considered whether the terms "volatile substance use" or "volatile substance misuse" might be more appropriate. However, we felt that the word "use" might be confusing because the products we are concerned with all have a "use" for which they were intended. As for "misuse", we felt that it would be unwise for us to attempt to change terminology when "volatile substance abuse" was now the generally accepted term. In this report the words "abuse" and "misuse" have the same meaning.

1.6 We do not cover the abuse of alkylnitrites (amyl and butyl nitrites, sometimes known as Rush, nitrites or poppers). Unlike the products misused in VSA, alkylnitrites are not marketed as household products in themselves and they do not cause intoxication. As a result, measures to tackle the problem of VSA would not necessarily be applicable to them.

1.7 In the introduction to our report on drug education in schools we defined "education about drugs" to refer to education about illegal drugs and misuse of medicinal products and volatile substances. Furthermore, although alcohol and tobacco are outside the remit of the Advisory Council, we recognised that much of drug education was relevant to the wider field of substance misuse including alcohol and tobacco and that it was sensible for drug education to be delivered in the context of an overall substance misuse approach. This applies generally to all preventive work: although different forms of substance misuse present different problems, the principles on which preventive work is based are broadly similar. In our 1990 report "Problem Drug Use: A Review of Training" [(3)], for example, we recommended that: "wherever possible trainers and training units should function on a substance problems basis rather than either drug or alcohol problems alone".

1.8 Nevertheless we felt that a specific report on VSA in our prevention series was justified because of the apparent extent and gravity of problems associated with VSA, the generally younger age range of misusers, the wide range of everyday household products which can be abused and the general tendency for VSA to receive less attention than other forms of substance misuse. And, whilst we recognised that many of the basic principles behind the recommendations in our report would be relevant across the range of substance misuse problems, we felt that some of these distinctive aspects of VSA merited specific attention.

Why we are concerned

1.9 We do not know how many young people misuse volatile substances but every year young people die from it. Many of those who die – up to 40% –

appear to be first-time users. From 1970 to 1990 the statistics show a steady increase in the number of deaths caused by VSA. By 1990, the number had reached 151 although, in the subsequent two years, it had reduced to 122 and then 79. The reduction is welcome but gives no cause for complacency. The majority of VSA deaths are of young people: the age range starts as young as nine years old and the commonest age of death is around 16 years. It is a major risk for young people. For example, in 1991, VSA accounted for one tenth of the deaths of 15 year old boys in the UK. In 1990, VSA was responsible for more deaths amongst 11 - 17 year olds than leukaemia, pneumonia and drowning combined (see chapter 2).

1.10 We do not know what proportion of all volatile substance misusers these death survey statistics represent. There have been a number of recent surveys of drug misuse among school-age children which produce varying results depending on a number of factors such as size of sample, age range, geographical area and so on. The Institute for the Study of Drug Dependence (ISDD)'s 1991 audit [4], drawing on several recent British studies, suggested that 4-8% of secondary school pupils might have tried volatile substances and that VSA was most common around the third and fourth years of secondary schooling. Whatever the exact figure, it is clear that a large number of young people are at risk either because they are already experimenting with VSA, or by association with peers who are involved in VSA. We return to the question of the extent of VSA in chapter 2.

Implications for society

1.11 In addition to the risk to the individual, VSA raises problems for families, schools, communities and for society at a national level. A young person might try VSA because of the influence of his or her peers: this can lead to experimentation spreading across whole groups of young people. The anxiety experienced by parents if they discover that their child is abusing these substances and the anguish parents suffer if their child suffers injury or death as a result cannot be overstated. There is also a cost to society from the interruption to a young person's education if their abuse of these substances leads to a deterioration in performance or absenteeism and from the costs of treating health-related problems. The unpredictable nature of outbreaks of VSA makes planning a response on the part of local services particularly difficult. Both schools and their localities may pay a heavy price if their reputation suffers as a result of being branded a "problem" area. While the majority of volatile substance abusers are not violent or aggressive, it seems clear that accidental self-harm may at times be a serious problem from VSA.

The history of VSA in the UK, and of Government action and legislation

1.12 There is little doubt that the rise in abuse of volatile substances can be partly attributed to the increased availability over recent years of household products which contain volatile substances and which can be misused. It has been estimated that the average household contains a dozen or more such products. Prior to 1970, although a few cases of VSA had been reported, it was not seen as being a serious problem in this country. In 1970 the police began to detect outbreaks of industrial chemical inhalation by young people, mainly in inner-city areas. The problem appeared to be confined to those areas for some years but, gradually, indiscriminate outbreaks, with no apparent geographical pattern, emerged in other parts of the UK. It is likely that, at the outset, the enjoyable effects of VSA were discovered accidentally. As time elapsed, however, and as young people became more knowledgeable of this phenomenon, a network of expertise built up until the stage was reached where it became common knowledge that the inhalation of certain fumes caused a change in awareness and mood.

1.13 By 1983 it was apparent that VSA had become a recognised area for concern. There were calls from many quarters, including Members of Parliament and the families of those who had been affected by it, for the Government to address the issue. Consequently, in that year, the Government undertook a consultation exercise with the police, the courts, drug agencies, MPs, local councils, parents, schools, the health service and retailers. The great majority of those who responded to the consultation felt that criminalising VSA would almost certainly be counterproductive, deterring misusers from seeking help and burdening many young people with a criminal record. It was also felt that criminalisation might put young people in even greater danger by leading them to abuse volatile substances in secret where, if help were needed, it might arrive too late. As a result, the Government decided not to make VSA an offence, although a legislative measure was introduced to control sales to minors. This was the Intoxicating Substances (Supply) Act 1985.

1.14 *The Intoxicating Substances (Supply) Act 1985* makes it an offence in the UK (except in Scotland) for a retailer to supply or offer to supply to persons under 18 years of age a substance (other than a controlled drug) "if he knows or has reasonable cause to believe that the substance or its fumes are likely to be inhaled . . . for the purpose of causing intoxication". The Act was introduced in Parliament as a Private Members' Bill by Mr Neville Trotter MP, with Government support, to remedy the weakness in English law revealed by a Scottish court case. In December 1983 two Glasgow shopkeepers were convicted of selling glue sniffing kits to children under Scottish common law which classifies, as criminal, wilful and reckless, actions which cause real injury to another person. No similar provision exists in either common law or statute law in England, Wales and Northern Ireland. The Intoxicating Substances (Supply) Act 1985 came into force in August 1985. The purpose of the Act was to stop those who knowingly or recklessly sold products to young volatile substance misusers for misuse. By 1992 there had been 60 prosecutions under the Act, 39 of which had resulted in findings of guilt. In the last year for which figures are available (1992) there were 5 prosecutions, 3 of which resulted in findings of guilt. Under the Act, an offender is liable to up to 6 months imprisonment or a maximum fine not exceeding level 5 on the standard scale (currently £5000) or both. It should be noted that shopkeepers are not obliged to display signs warning against VSA, though the National Federation of Retail Newsagents issues to all its members a poster warning that the newsagent reserves the right not to supply certain products if they believe they will be misused, and many other stores display signs.

1.15 In Scotland, as explained above, common law provides for a similar offence of "recklessly" selling volatile substances to children knowing they are going to inhale them. Furthermore, *the Solvent Abuse (Scotland) Act 1983* was introduced to amend the Social Work (Scotland) Act 1968 by adding solvent abuse to the conditions indicating the need for compulsory measures of care for a child who "has misused a volatile substance by deliberately inhaling, other than for medicinal purposes, that substance's vapour".

1.16 Other pieces of legislation have bearings on volatile substance abuse either directly or indirectly. Some of these are described below.

1.17 Certain sections of *the Children Act 1989* have potential implications for young people who abuse volatile substances and their families. Section 17 requires local authorities to safeguard and promote the welfare of children within their area who are in need (being unable to achieve or maintain a reasonable standard of health or development or if health or development are significantly impaired) and to promote the upbringing of such children by their families.

1.18 Local authorities are required to provide a range of services to meet needs in their area. These services may include counselling and advice and social or recreational activities. In families where VSA by children or parents is prejudicing the welfare of children, the local authority should see these children as children in need and therefore eligible for services. Services should be provided in partnership with parents and young people.

1.19 In exceptional circumstances where VSA is causing or likely to cause significant harm to children, a child protection investigation may be necessary under Section 47 of the Children Act 1989.

1.20 In Scotland, Section 12 of *the Social Work (Scotland) Act 1968* provides powers broadly similar to those of section 17 of the Children Act 1989. It places a general duty on local authorities in Scotland to promote social welfare by making available advice, guidance and assistance on a scale appropriate for their area. In practice, authorities provide a range of services which may include counselling, advice, assistance in kind or, exceptionally and subject to certain conditions, in cash.

1.21 It is recognised that a child may be in need of compulsory measures of care if he or she has misused a volatile substance by inhaling its vapour, other than for medicinal purposes. This, therefore, represents a specific ground under Section 32(2)(gg) of the Social Work (Scotland) Act 1968 for the referral of a child to a children's hearing which would give consideration to the steps necessary to ensure his or her protection, control, guidance and treatment.

1.22 Also in Scotland, if the child was likely to be caused unnecessary suffering or serious impairment of health because there was a lack of parental care, which might stem from the parent's abuse of volatile substances, the child could, where necessary, under Section 37 of the 1968 Act, be taken to a place of safety. In any event, where it appears that the child needs compulsory measures of care, arrangements would be made for a hearing to consider what steps should be taken.

1.23 In Northern Ireland, childcare law is being revised to bring it broadly into line with the position in England and Wales under the Children Act 1989. Until the new legislation becomes law, *the Children and Young Persons Act (Northern Ireland) 1968* will continue to apply. Section 164 of the Act places a general duty on Health and Social Service Boards and Health and Social Service Trusts to provide advice, guidance and assistance in order to promote the welfare of children by reducing the need to bring them into care or to court.

1.24 There are also measures that can be taken if a person commits an offence whilst intoxicated by volatile substances such as:

(i) *Section 5 of the Public Order Act 1986* enables the police to take action against people who abuse solvents in public if they are disorderly or abusive. This Act extends only to England and Wales. In Scotland, the police would deal with similar situations under common law with the offence of breach of the peace. In Northern Ireland, broadly similar powers exist under Article 18 of *the Public Order (Northern Ireland) Act 1987*.

(ii) In some circumstances, prosecutions may be brought for offences which apply only in particular places. For example, under a British Rail byelaw, it is an offence to be intoxicated on railway property. Under *the Licensing (Scotland) Act 1976*, licensing boards are empowered to introduce byelaws, subject to the terms of those being approved by the Secretary of State. Some local boards have byelaws applying in designated public places (eg within a specified radius of the local football ground or within a public park) but these are aimed primarily at the consumption of alcohol.

(iii) If a person commits an offence under the influence of drugs or solvents there are provisions under Paragraph 6 of Schedule 1a of *the Criminal Justice Act 1991* for a judge or magistrate to decide to recommend by court order that the person receive treatment as part of a community sentence.

(iv) *The Road Traffic Act 1988* enables the police to take action against a person who drives, attempts to drive, or is in charge of a mechanically propelled vehicle whilst unfit to drive because of drink or drugs. For the purposes of this Act, any substance taken into the body which is not a drink and is not taken as a food and which affects the control of the human body is considered to be a drug. Similar provisions apply in respect of railway workers under *the Transport and Works Act 1992*. In Northern Ireland, similar provisions are contained in *the Road Traffic (Northern Ireland) Order 1981*.

1.25 Instead of introducing further legislation, the Government has, in recent years, felt that the main focus of its strategy to tackle VSA should be on educational and preventive measures. The main thrust of its strategy has been to provide parents and professional staff, such as doctors, teachers, youth workers and social workers, with the sort of knowledge and skills which would enable them to educate young people in the dangers of misuse, to dissuade them from experimenting and to help those who had already misused volatile substances. The Government's initiatives have included:

- the production of a training film for professionals working with young people;
- the issue (in 1984) of a Home Office circular to police forces setting out the various options and facilities open to them when they came into contact with volatile substance misusers;
- the production of a leaflet for parents and professionals by the Health Education Authority;
- the issue of guidelines to retailers;
- grant support to Local Education Authorities for preventive health education programmes.

1.26 More recent initiatives include:

- a number of Department of Health (DH) grants to Re-Solv (the leading voluntary organisation on VSA);
- Department of Trade and Industry funding to Re-Solv for a new retail training video pack;
- projects by Home Office Drug Prevention Teams;
- DH funding to St George's Hospital Medical School to research and collate VSA mortality data;
- DH funding to the National Children's Bureau to support its Solvent Misuse Project;
- a DH grant to the Institute for the Study of Drug Dependence towards a distance learning pack for professionals;
- The Government's 1992 national anti-solvent television campaign aimed at raising parental awareness of VSA;
- The Government's 1994 campaign to help parents talk to their children about drug and VSA, with advice on sources of help if needed.

1.27 European Drug Prevention Week, in October 1994, aimed to raise awareness in the UK of drug and VSA, particularly by young people. We commend these initiatives and go on in later chapters to consider the future of prevention and treatment activities.

Changes in legislation

1.28 We have considered whether it would be appropriate to recommend any further legislation in this area, and have concluded that it would not. Despite the fact that the Intoxicating Substances (Supply) Act is difficult to enforce, we cannot conceive of any acceptable legislative changes which would do more than this Act does to help protect young people. Indeed, it has been suggested that one of the results of the Act was to divert some young people from glue sniffing to the inhalation of other, perhaps more dangerous, substances. We do not know to what extent this was true but the unpredictable consequences of legislation in this area reinforces our inclination not to recommend change.

Recommendations

1. **VSA should be accorded greater salience on community agendas and professional concerns** (Preface)

2. **VSA today constitutes a topic worthy of focused attention in its own right** (1.4)

3. **We do not believe that any further enactments would at present be helpful in controlling VSA** (1.28)

CHAPTER 2

CAUSES, PREVALENCE AND PATTERNS

Introduction

2.1 The aim of this chapter is to establish as best possible what is known about the causes of volatile substance abuse (VSA), its prevalence, and the different patterns of use which may occur. The discussion is structured in the following way. First a brief note is given on the types of evidence on which we rely. Then we examine an array of possible factors which may incline the individual to use volatile substances. The next section looks at patterns of use both in terms of frequency and duration, and coincidental use of other drugs. Data on prevalence follow in relation to general school age populations and some special population groups. Data on deaths resulting from VSA are presented in the following Section. VSA in other countries is then examined. Finally, some of the main conclusions which can be drawn from this review are brought into focus.

2.2 We want this report to be readily intelligible to a wide audience and hope therefore that no-one will be put off by the fact that in this particular chapter it has been seen as necessary to cite authorities and give references, thus rooting what is being said in the available research literature. We felt that it would be unsatisfactory to give opinions without the supporting evidence.

The type of information on which we rely and the shortage of information

2.3 The development of effective measures to address VSA depends upon ar accurate assessment of the size of the problem, the personal and social characteristics of the users, and the social context of use. Data are also needed on the substances of abuse, the mode of use, and the reasons for VSA; the relationship between VSA and abuse of alcohol, tobacco and other drugs; and mortality statistics. We need the developmental and longitudinal pictures which describe VSA in the individual's life course. More needs to be known about psychological effects which are sought or achieved with these kinds of intoxication.

2.4 Other than for data on mortality which have been gathered on an annual basis by the Department of Public Health Sciences and Toxicology Unit at St. George's Hospital Medical School, London, since 1971, no national information on VSA of the kind outlined above is available in the UK on a systematic or repeat basis. The picture has to be pieced together from a number of sample surveys which have looked, in general, at drug-taking among young people and dealt with VSA in passing, from some formal research conducted at local level, and from more anecdotal sources. We believe that it is possible thus to assemble a useful outline picture, but the gaps in information are very large.

2.5 There is also international literature on VSA which is applicable at the toxicology level. But all overseas research conducted on the social and behavioural aspects of VSA is usually less reliable for application in the UK, given that VSA as a behaviour is so embedded in the social context.

Volatile substance abuse: predisposing factors

2.6 Research from the wider drugs field suggests that adolescent drug use is a function of a range of diverse social and psychological stressors and risk factors (1) with multiple pathways to substance use (2). Hawkins and colleagues, in a recent review of risk factors associated with alcohol and other drug problems (3), suggest a variety of predisposing factors, not all of which have as yet been fully examined in relation to VSA. These include such factors as:

- neighbourhood disorganisation;
- poor family management strategies;
- family conflict;
- low bonding and poor relationships with family;
- low academic achievement;
- early and persistent problem behaviours;
- low commitment and bonding to school;
- peer rejection in early school years;
- alienation and rebelliousness;
- favourable attitudes to drug use;
- early initiation into drug use.

These predisposing factors implicated in the abuse of licit and illicit substances generally, could also be expected to help precipitate VSA.

2.7 One of the main limitations on reviewing literature on predisposing factors is the lack of consistency in concepts and operational definitions across the various studies published. This creates difficulty when trying to identify common factors across studies. It has contributed to the lack of understanding of the relative weight of particular factors or of how factors, or sets of factors, interact in predisposing an individual towards VSA.

Sensation seeking and curiosity

2.8 Adolescents are at a time in their lives when the urge to try out new experiences and sensations is intense. Some young people may be attracted by the excitement and the element of danger involved in the use of volatile substances. Faber, in a 1985 study of 597 secondary school abusers [4], found that, for 34.5% of them, curiosity was the main motivating force behind their VSA. VSA may also be seen as an act of rebellion – a means of shocking parents and of announcing the passing of childhood.

Socially determined reasons

2.9 Ashton [5] suggests that, whilst volatile substance abusers may come from any socioeconomic group, children from lower socioeconomic sectors and disrupted families are over-represented. There is empirical evidence to support the view that abusers experience more adverse circumstances than non-abusers. Some illustrative reports are as follows:

- Sourindhrin and Baird [6] reported on 134 clinic attending sniffers and 100 non-sniffers, matched for age and sex, and found that only 63% of the sniffers had both parents living together compared with 83% of the non-sniffers, and that 51% of the sniffers' fathers were unemployed compared with 23% of the non-sniffers' fathers;

- Faber [4] found, in her studies in the East Sussex Health Authority District, that the locality which recorded the highest percentage of long-term abusers had low socioeconomic status and an almost total absence of recreational and social facilities;

- Chadwick, Anderson and Yule [7], in their study of 105 solvent abusing schoolchildren, found that abusers were slightly less likely to be living with both natural parents than non-abusers. They were more likely to come from families living in rented accommodation, and significantly more likely to have many siblings.

Psychological reasons

2.10 Some work suggests that VSA may represent an attempt on the part of a young person to escape temporarily from reality and to blot out any problems which he or she may be experiencing in life (Masterson [8], Biggs,

Bender and Foreman [9], Gardiner and Biddle [10], Ives [11]). Edeh [12] suggests that loss or bereavement may be a cause in some cases. Zur and Yule [13] found that a history of extreme family adversity, including psychiatric illness and early death or suicide of a parent, and child abuse, was more common amongst solvent abusers than non-abusers. They also found that the number of solvent abusers who could remember family disharmony at an early age, or who could not remember ever having seen their father, was double that of non-abusers. Sourindhrin [14] suggests that VSA constitutes a form of social activity which 'caters to the needs for acceptance, status, and regard of children who feel lonely, rejected or friendless'. Richardson [15] suggests that VSA may appeal to children who have low self-esteem, who feel lonely, isolated or 'different', or who feel socially awkward, blame other people for their misfortune and who cannot talk about how they feel.

Demographic factors

2.11 An examination of the ages and sexes of abusers, based on the limited information available, might help in our understanding of the problem. The peak ages for VSA seem to be 14-15. In Stuart's study of 1729 school pupils aged 11-18 [16], the peak ages for experimentation with solvents were 14-15, with 12% of the respondents of that age reporting ever use. Cooke's survey of 4474 school pupils aged 11-19 [17] revealed that, of those who had tried glue sniffing, 11% had started by age 11 and 58% by age 13. Reports of the sex ratio of VSA are variable. Stuart [16] reported a male:female ratio of 3:1, while Diamond, [18] found that solvent abusers were slightly more likely to be male than female. Cooke [17], showed a male:female ratio of 2.3:1. However, Swadi's survey of 3,073 pupils aged 11-16 [19] suggested that girls might be beginning to overtake boys in terms of 'ever trying' volatile substances. It is probable, in our opinion, that boys are more likely than girls to become long-term solvent abusers, and it is possible that girls are equally as likely as boys, if not more so, to be experimental users. What is clear, however, is that VSA kills nearly nine times as many boys as girls [20]. It is also clear that the gap between the proportion of male deaths and female deaths grows with increasing age.

Accessibility

2.12 One obvious but highly important reason for use is probably "because it's there". Thus Ramsey and his colleagues [21] point out that the widespread availability of these abusable substances may do much to explain their continued popularity, in that they are readily found around the house, they are affordable, concealable, and easy to steal. They also provide a cheap alternative to alcohol, are not illegal, and have the added advantage of providing a quick effect and a rapid recovery, which might be indispensable for young people who need to return home sober in order to conceal their habit. O'Connor [22] suggests that the gains from use include emotional comfort and the relief of stress as well as a disinhibiting effect on the personality – all of which may hold an appeal for the young person. The anticipation of hallucinations is also perceived as being a powerful motivator: dealing with the type of experience may give the young person a sense of control which he or she lacks in the rest of his or her life.

Peer group pressure

2.13 The peer group is widely acknowledged to be particularly influential during adolescence. Young people, because of the desire to emulate their friends and the need to gain group membership and approval, may engage in VSA because it is the approved group activity of the moment. 15% of those studied by Faber [4] said that they had experimented in order to be like friends. In Cooke, Evans and Farrow's study [17], 18% of the 207 abusers who responded said that they had been persuaded to try glue sniffing; 4% said that they had been coerced into trying. Another conclusion can be drawn from this last statement – that 96% of the abusers had not been coerced into trying. It ought to be said, too, that peer groups can act as a positive influence – peer group pressure might, just as easily, encourage people not to sniff.

Patterns and modes of use

2.14 Masterson [8] considers that experimenters constitute by far the largest group of solvent abusers. There is a fairly general consensus that users can be seen as falling into three broad groups – the experimenters who are common, the controlled, episodic, users who are not uncommon, and the chronic users who are a much smaller group. In reality one is dealing with a range of use rather than with discreet categories. Experimenters can be defined as those who sniff once or only on a few occasions. The controlled users are those who use regularly over a limited period, but who continue to view their use as a social activity. Parrott [23] suggests that the controlled episodic use of volatile substances is similar to alcohol use amongst some groups of older adolescents. The habitual or chronic user, according to Parrot, may have been originally introduced to solvent abuse as part of a group but, as their use increases, they begin to abuse solvents while alone or display a pattern of both solitary and group use. Watson [24] reported that groups of habitual users tended to include users of differing ages, drawn from different localities, who got together simply for the purpose of abusing solvents. Chronic users can spend several hours each day in an intoxicated state.

2.15 There is some empirical support for the suggestion that VSA occurs mainly as a group activity. Sourindhrin and Baird [6], in their study of 134 users referred to a police clinic in Glasgow, found that 92.5% of them abused volatile substances as a group activity, 5.2% both as part of a group and as a solitary activity, and 2.2% were solitary abusers. Of the 20 solvent abusing delinquents studied by Jacobs and Ghodse [25], 15 usually inhaled with friends and 16 usually inhaled out of doors. 12 inhaled solvents on three days or more per week and 10 for more than five hours per day. Lockhart and Lennox [26] reported that VSA was a group activity for the majority of the sniffers in both their secure unit and community samples. Evans and Raistrick [27], in a study comparing 31 toluene and 12 butane gas abusers, found that the majority of the glue sniffers did so in a group setting (mainly because they were afraid of the consequences of doing it on their own), while most of the gas sniffers sniffed alone at least sometimes. 50% of both groups sniffed on a daily basis.

2.16 Information on the modes of VSA tends to be rather anecdotal. Solvent vapour may be inhaled by various techniques which are designed to increase the available concentration [(5)]. Glue is generally poured into a plastic bag – supermarket bags are widely used – and the bag is then placed over the nose and mouth or over the whole head. This is known as 'huffing'. According to Ives [(11)], the bag is sometimes squeezed in order to heat up the glue and allow the volatile hydrocarbons to evaporate more rapidly. Air may be breathed into the bag – the carbon dioxide reportedly helps to increase the 'buzz'. Liquids, such as dry-cleaning fluids and thinners, are inhaled from their containers or poured onto rags or items of clothing before inhalation. Large bags are sometimes filled with gas from aerosols, fire extinguishers and fuel gases, and the contents inhaled [(21)]. The contents of cigarette lighter refills are also sprayed directly into the mouth.

2.17 Use may occur in secluded public areas such as a corner of a park, a multi-storey car park, or a derelict house. Bus shelters, railway lines and canal banks are other possible sites. However, VSA also takes place in the home setting. Indeed, Taylor and her colleagues [(20)] reveal that 64% of those who died from VSA in 1992 abused the fatal substance in their home or in the home of a friend, and that 45% of them actually died in their own home or in that of a friend.

2.18 Little research has been carried out into whether VSA is likely to lead into use of other drugs. Indeed, only one study of which we are aware has actually examined the issue of progression. Davies and her colleagues [(28)] presented the case histories of four solvent abusers who progressed from using solvents to illicit drugs. Each of the four individuals had suffered parental rejection or deprivation in childhood and three had suffered physical abuse. All had been chronic users of solvents, and all progressed from sniffing glue to smoking heroin. Life events, economic factors, the availability of illicit drugs and peer group pressure are all thought to have played a role in the transition process. These case reports are interesting but clearly only a small fraction of solvent abusers will progress onto a major drug problem. What is also clear is that there is a need for longitudinal studies which could reveal more not only about the numbers who progress but also about the mechanisms involved. Alcohol and cigarettes are also very much part of the overall picture [29].

Estimating the extent of the problem

2.19 The epidemiology of drug abuse in general faces several difficulties. For example, it can be difficult to define adequately cases or categories of use. The illicit nature of drug taking makes the task of establishing its prevalence very complicated. Self-reported data can be unreliable. There are sampling difficulties and the truants who are absent from the class on the day of the school survey may have among them many of the drug users. The fact that such truants are perhaps absent from surveys should be borne in mind when trying to draw conclusions from questionnaire research. The same difficulties apply in trying to estimate the prevalence of VSA, even though, unlike drug misuse, it is not illegal.

2.20 Studies designed to estimate the prevalence of VSA have usually taken one of two forms. Firstly, what can be termed 'general population' surveys have been conducted using samples drawn either from schools or randomly selected households. The focus of these surveys has been either drug use in general (including volatile substances) or VSA alone. Secondly, 'selected population' studies have been conducted. These studies have focused on levels of abuse among delinquents and young people referred to drug treatment agencies, or to specific care and educational institutions.

2.21 Ives [30] has identified some 23 school surveys conducted in the UK since the 1970s. Many of these were localised, or involved small sample sizes and concentrated on 15 and 16 year olds. There have, however, been larger surveys undertaken in different geographical areas and focusing on a wider age range. We give a selective summary below of some of the more important findings deriving from this work:

- Faber [4] carried out a survey on a random sample of school children in nine secondary schools in the East Sussex Health Authority district in March 1983. Of the 7343 pupils (aged 11-18) surveyed, 8.1% reported that they had abused solvents in the previous year;

- Stuart [16] surveyed 1729 pupils aged 11 to 18 attending nine comprehensive schools, and a single-sex fee paying school, in one health district in the north west of England. She found that 108 (6%) had experimented with solvents but 17% of the sample was absent when the questionnaires were handed out. Of the 108, 62 had experimented with solvents only. The remainder had also experimented with an unspecified additional drug;

- two sequential surveys were carried out by Diamond and colleagues [18] in 1985 and 1986, and involved three schools in Bournemouth and Poole, and three in Southampton. They were designed to explore the incidence of drug and solvent abuse in fourth and fifth year comprehensive school children (aged 15 and 16). The sample sizes were 807 in 1985 and 602 in 1986, and achieved a response rate of 90% and 84% respectively. The authors report that the incidence of drug and solvent misuse did not vary between the two dates. In all, 10% of the sample reported having used solvents alone and a further but uncertain percentage had used other drugs in addition;

- Swadi's survey [19] of 3,333 adolescents in six comprehensive schools in London enquired about the frequency of current use of cigarettes, alcohol, solvents and illicit drugs. Completed questionnaires were collected from 3,073 pupils aged between 11 and 16 years, of whom 11% admitted to ever having used solvents. 8% of the total sample reported that they had tried solvents only once. 0.78% said that they were weekly users and only 0.65% said that they were daily users;

- Cooke and others [17] in South Wales employed a sample of 4921 pupils aged 11 to 19, of whom 4474 returned completed questionnaires. 6.8%

admitted to ever having tried glue sniffing. Only 0.7%, however, were current sniffers. Glue sniffing had been tried by children from each of the 28 schools taking part in the survey but 'ever use' prevalence rates varied from 1.4% to 14% between schools;

- Chadwick and colleagues [31] screened pupils aged 13 to 16, at 16 London schools, by means of a self-report questionnaire in order to find out how many had engaged in VSA. A total of 7845 pupils were eligible for inclusion in the study. 11% were excluded at the request of their parents and 15.8% were absent when the questionnaire was administered. Completed questionnaires were obtained from 5014 pupils, of whom 4.1% indicated that, at some time, they had abused volatile substances to the point of intoxication. However, when interviews were conducted with 133 of these, only 106 confirmed their use of volatile substances;

- Balding carried out a non-random survey of 23,928 pupils aged between 12 and 16 in 142 self-nominated schools throughout England, in 1991 [32]. This was the sixth in a series based on a Health Related Behaviour Questionnaire. The sample represented approximately 22% of the total population of the schools used. The survey covered a number of health related areas – diet, doctor and dentist, health and safety, home, drugs, money, sport, and social and personal. Questions about solvents made up only a small part of the drugs section, and questions were only asked about ever use. The pupils were asked 'have you ever taken any of these drugs?', and a list of drugs, including 'solvents', was given. 4.47% of all respondents answered yes to solvents. There was an increase in the number of respondents answering yes as their age increased. For Year 8 pupils (aged 12-13), only 1.84% answered yes whereas, for year 11 pupils (aged 15-16) 8.23% did. Yes responses were fewer from girls than from boys in years 8 and 9 (aged 12-14) but higher in years 10 and 11 (aged 14-16).

2.22 Three recent general population household surveys have contained sections on self-reported drug use, including VSA. The 1992 British Crime Survey [33], which was a representative national sample of over 10,000 individuals, indicated that lifetime usage of "glue, gas or aerosols" was most common amongst 16 to 19 year old respondents (6%). Between 1% of 12 to 13 year olds, 2% of 14 to 15 year olds and 2% of 16 to 19 year olds reported trying solvents in the last year. The Four Cities Drug Prevention Survey [34] focused on a random sample of 4,000 people aged 16+ and a booster sample of 1,000 young people aged 16 – 25 at "high risk of drug use" across the four British cities selected. The proportion of respondents who had ever tried "sniffing glue, gas or aerosols" was in the range of 0 – 2% in the main sample and between 0 – 6% in the booster sample. The 1993 Scottish Crime Survey, which was a representative sample of 5,000 individuals across Scotland, revealed that 1 – 2% of the sample had ever taken solvents, with women aged 16 – 19 (7%) and men aged 20 – 24 (6%) forming the largest groups.

2.23 Parker and Measham [35] surveyed 752 schoolchildren age 15 – 16 from four schools in Merseyside and Greater Manchester. 13% of the sample reported lifetime usage of solvents. 7% had used in the past year and 3% had used in the last month.

2.24 It should be noted that there are a number of ways used to describe VSA in the résumés in this chapter – VSA, solvent abuse and glue sniffing. They may not all refer to exactly the same phenomenon and we have therefore adopted the terminology used by the author of each survey. The reader may wish to bear this in mind when comparing the surveys.

2.25 Studies of special populations are of interest in their own right and show where the problems tend to be concentrated. The young people involved in these surveys inevitably tend though to be atypical abusers in that they have come to the attention of the police or other agencies either because of their VSA or because they have engaged in problematic behaviour:

in Parker's study [36], designed to assess the number of problem drug users known to a variety of agencies in Bristol over the period March 1984 to February 1985, 17% of the 759 drug users identified had problems associated with solvents;

- Allison and Jerrom [37] reported that 80% of the 65 male adolescent offenders in three institutional schools in the west of Scotland had inhaled solvents at least once;

- Lockhart and Lennox [26] compared 23 adolescent boys referred to a secure unit in Northern Ireland with a group of 27 boys from a similar background living in the community. Approximately two-thirds of the institution sample admitted to having been involved in VSA as compared with one-third of the community sample. Significantly more of the institution sample were habitual users;

- in their study of 47 consecutive admissions to a secure unit of a regional assessment centre in West London, Jacobs and Ghodse [25] found that 20 of the 47 were regular solvent abusers.

Children looked after by the local authority

2.26 Children who are looked after by the local authority and who are fostered or in residential accommodation are as susceptible to VSA as any other child or young person, particularly when peer group pressure is taken into consideration. The link between emotional vulnerability and VSA must be noted and such vulnerability would apply to most of the care population.

2.27 Information supplied by the National Childrens Bureau suggests that children in residential homes are more likely to sniff solvents than are other children. A survey of sniffing deaths by Anderson et al [38] found that 10% of those under 18 who had died as a result of VSA were defined as "in care" - a much higher proportion than would be expected by chance. Paragraph 2.9 of this chapter refers to research which suggests that disrupted families and family problems are potential pre-disposing factors towards VSA, and it is therefore not unreasonable to presume that children who are looked after by the local authority are more vulnerable to VSA.

Children in Child Guidance Clinics

2.28 There is very little epidemiologic data about volatile substance abusers and child mental health clinic attenders. In the only recent available study [(39)] volatile substance abusers comprised 3% of all referrals to a child guidance clinic and 7.9% of adolescent referrals. For most clinics this would amount to about 20 – 25 cases per year. As a proportion of referrals at each age there was only a slight rise between ages 12 to 16 but, in overall numbers, the largest proportion of abusers presented at age 14.

2.29 It is very likely that volatile substance abusers attending child guidance clinics are not representative of all teenage abusers. In the same study, Swadi [(39)] reported that only 22% were referred for VSA whilst the rest had a variety of reasons for referral, mainly 'behavioural problems' (33%), but ranging from deliberate self-harm to sexual abuse. Volatile substance abusers have a higher rate of depression, particularly for girls, though the direction of any causal link has yet to be determined. Community based studies find lower rates of co-morbidity but there is evidence that volatile substance abusers are over-represented in other at risk groups including conduct disorder and delinquency and in institutions.

2.30 There are mixed reports about the families of volatile substance abusers. The prevalence of VSA in children of intact coping families is not known. VSA is associated with family dysfunction, parental divorce and single parent families [(19)]. The nature of any causal relationships are unclear and certainly complex. There is evidence, however, that parental attitude to substance abuse is related to substance abuse in general though parents are possibly less aware of the likelihood of VSA and of the associated dangers than of other substance abuse.

Mortality

2.31 Pottier et al [(40)] suggest that population mortality associated with VSA may be related to many factors, including the chemical nature of the substances abused, the product containing the volatile substance, the method of inhalation and the prevalence of abuse. Shepherd [41] noted that individuals who abuse volatile substances may die in a number of ways. He categorised those deaths which occur during exposure or in the minutes or hours afterwards as 'acute' deaths. These deaths may be directly related to inhalation or they may be the result of a secondary event such as trauma. Deaths might also theoretically occur months or years after exposure but still be directly related to the magnitude and duration of exposure. An example of this would be death due to liver or renal failure if the reality of such risk is established.

2.32 One of four mechanisms may be involved as causes of acute death associated with VSA. These are anoxia (oxygen deficiency), vagal inhibition (inhibition of the vagus nerve which runs between the brain and the heart), respiratory depression and cardiac arrythmia (variation of the heart's rhythm). Each may be involved in any death and it is only by considering the sequence of events and method of inhalation that the most likely cause of death can be established [40]. Anoxia can occur due to inhalation of vomit or because a plastic bag has been placed over the head. Vagal inhibition is associated with butane and aerosol propellants being sprayed directly into the throat and causing acute cooling. Respiratory depression can be a consequence of the overall depression of the central nervous system. Cardiac arrhythmias are thought to be the most likely cause of acute direct deaths, and may result from sensitisation of the heart muscle to adrenaline. Indirect causes of death include falls and other accidents.

2.33 The principal substances causing death are fuel gases (generally butane), solvents in adhesives (toluene), other solvents such as 1,1,1-trichloroethane, and aerosol propellants, with the first three each accounting for about 30% of deaths [21]. Accidents or suicide have been implicated in about half the deaths associated with toluene abuse, but only about 2-3% of deaths associated with other volatile substances.

2.34 A VSA death is defined as one which would not have occurred if the deceased had not abused a volatile substance, regardless of what was the terminal event. Death data for the UK are collated by the St George's Hospital Medical School team, which we mentioned earlier. The methods for data collection have been relatively stable since 1983. Data are obtained from a number of sources, including press clippings agencies; HM Coroners; the Crown Office in Scotland; the Lord Chancellor's Office in Northern Ireland; the Deputy Viscount of Jersey; HM Greffier of Guernsey; the High Bailiff of the Isle of Man, the Office of Population, Censuses and Surveys (OPCS); the National Poisons Unit, the Home Office Forensic Science Laboratories; the Health and Safety Executive; the Railways Inspectorate; and from ad hoc notifications. Accurately recording VSA deaths requires an innovative technique because of the many ways in which death can occur. We can see no obvious changes to the current procedures which would improve current recording of VSA deaths except, perhaps, if coroners were to note any connection with volatile substances in their additional comments in part IV of the notification forms. This would enable the case to be picked up by the OPCS on its supplementary digit system.

2.35 The latest report on mortality from the St George's team, which we mentioned earlier, covers the period 1971 to the end of 1992 [20].

2.36 The total number of deaths recorded from 1971 to the end of 1992 was 1317. The number of deaths had been increasing since the early 80s – between 1983 and 1990 this was equivalent on average to an increase of 8.9% per year. From 1985 to 1991 at least 100 people died each year as a result of VSA, reaching a peak of 151 in 1990. In 1991 and 1992 the numbers fell to 122 and 79. These falls are welcome but should not be allowed to lead to a let-up in action against VSA. Too much should not be made of any one year's figures. Deaths are still occurring in unacceptable numbers.

2.37 Deaths associated with VSA comprise an important proportion of all deaths in young people. The age range of those who have died as a result of VSA is 9 to 76 years, but 60.7% of all deaths have occurred in the 14-18 age group; 72.6% were of people aged under 20. 88% of deaths have occurred in males. There appear to be no significant trends in age and sex distribution, although there has been a slight upward trend in deaths among girls.

2.38 Northern Ireland has the highest mortality rate (11.7 per million of the population aged 10 – 24). In absolute terms, however, the highest number of deaths since 1971 have been recorded in the south east of England.

2.39 Gas fuels have been the primary substances implicated in 36.2% of all deaths since 1971; aerosols in 20.6%; and glues in 18.9%. Since 1971, 53.9% of deaths have been attributable to the direct toxic effects of the substances being abused. Since the early 1980s there has been a general decrease in deaths resulting from plastic bags being placed over the head.

2.40 Of the people who died in 1992, 24.1% either died on the first occasion of abuse, or there was no evidence of previous abuse. In 1991, the figure was 37.75%. Figures for 1991 also reveal that the place where the substance was abused prior to death is fairly evenly divided between indoors and public places such as parks and shopping centres.

2.41 To help put the mortality problems of VSA into perspective, we have made comparisons of the number of deaths caused by VSA with the number of deaths due to three other causes – leukaemia, pneumonia and drowning. We chose these three because they are common and well-known causes of death among young people. We have concentrated our comparisons on deaths of those aged 10 – 18. We have already explained in chapter one that VSA is, for certain ages, a bigger killer than leukaemia, pneumonia and drowning combined and that, for certain ages, it constitutes a significant proportion of all deaths. The table below, covering 1991, sets out our findings.

Deaths by age and cause 1991 United Kingdom

	all causes			VSA			leukaemia			pneumonia			drowning		
age	m	f	tot	m	f	tot	m	f	tot	m	f	tot	m	f	tot
10	68	50	118	0	0	0	4	4	8	3	2	5	1	0	1
11	68	52	120	1	0	1	5	4	9	0	1	1	0	0	0
12	66	48	114	3	3	6	3	3	6	1	0	1	1	0	1
13	94	39	133	3	3	6	3	0	3	1	2	3	1	1	2
14	109	75	184	8	4	12	4	5	9	0	2	2	2	0	2
15	161	72	233	16	3	19	6	0	6	0	0	0	5	0	5
16	206	84	290	16	0	16	3	2	5	2	1	3	3	0	3
17	280	130	410	7	0	7	8	4	12	2	2	4	5	0	5
18	382	108	490	9	3	12	4	2	6	4	0	4	8	1	9
Total	1434	658	2092	63	16	79	40	24	64	13	10	23	26	2	28

VSA in other countries

2.42 VSA is not generally perceived to be as great a problem in the rest of Europe, but it is not clear whether this is due to lack of data and information for measuring the problem or because the problem is genuinely less acute. In 1991-92 the Pompidou Group of the Council of Europe sent a questionnaire on VSA to its member countries and published a report on the responses received. Only three countries other than the UK submitted data on VSA deaths (Denmark, Finland and Belgium), all of which had much lower figures. Only five countries other than the UK (Denmark, Norway, Belgium, Switzerland and the Netherlands) submitted any prevalence data. However, Republic of Ireland data suggest that they experience a roughly equivalent proportion of deaths as a percentage of the total population in comparison with the UK. The lack of data from other countries and the lower figures from Denmark, Finland and Belgium may be attributable to the fact that death recording systems are not comparable to those in the UK or that other countries simply might not collect VSA death data separately.

2.43 A survey in Japan [42], involving 5,250 12-15 year olds, carried out in November 1990, found that 1.5% of the subjects admitted to VSA (2.1% boys and 0.9% of girls). VSA was found to be strongly associated with alcohol and cigarette consumption (despite the fact that neither are, legally, available to those under 20 years of age) and with delinquent behaviour. A survey carried out in 1990 in New Zealand [43] showed that approximately 2% of respondents aged 14-18 had abused volatile substances. In Australia, the 1991 National Campaign Against Drug Abuse household survey, which involved 2,500 people aged 14 years and over, found that 1% of them had used inhalants in the past year. However, a survey of 'street kids' in Sydney, aged 14 – 19, indicated that 84% of them had tried inhalants. In the period 1980 – 88 there were 133 deaths in Australia attributable to VSA.

2.44 Although there is a lack of substantive statistical data, VSA seems to be widespread in South America, though it is mainly confined to poor areas. In Paraguay, for example, volatile substances are regarded as 'the poor peoples' drug' because they are only used by young people from poor areas. It is estimated that 80 – 85% of 'street' children in Paraguay have practised VSA. In Colombia, VSA is widespread amongst the poor, sometimes for its cold and hunger suppressing effects. In Brazil, VSA is rife among street children. Surveys from Brasilia and Sao Paulo suggest that the vast majority of street children abuse volatile substances. Shoemaker's glue is a popular substance of abuse [44].

2.45 In the USA, the National Household Survey on Drug Use found that, in 1990, 7 – 8% of those aged 12 – 17 admitted to having used volatile substances [45]. However, a national survey involving 15,760 high school students found that 16.6% of the students admitted having ever used them.

Recommendations

1. The available research amply demonstrates that VSA is a rather common but complex, socially embedded problem, affecting many different young people for different reasons and in varying degrees. Only that vision of complexity will serve society well when designing responses (2.4 – 2.5)

2. A strengthened and more informed response to VSA will require improved understanding of causes, patterns and prevalence. We recommend that the current relative neglect of social and epidemiological research on this topic should be remedied and hope that the Department of Health will take the lead in stimulating and co-ordinating a research initiative. Mortality data provide a valuable epidemiological indicator, and support for the St George's team should be continued. There would be benefit if coroners were to note any connection with VSA in the additional comments which are given by them in Part IV of notification forms (2.34)

CHAPTER 3

TOXICOLOGY

Volatile substances as chemical hazards: the scope of this chapter

3.1 This chapter is about the chemicals which are found in abused products and which, when deliberately inhaled, find their way into the blood and the brain and produce the effects sought during volatile substance abuse (VSA). We consider that, in trying to understand the problems associated with VSA, it is vital to have an understanding of the nature and effects of the substances which are abused. We therefore urge the reader not to miss out this chapter.

3.2 As with Chapter 2, we have cited authorities and given references in order to justify what we say. So far as possible, however, we have used non-technical language to give an account of the effects of these substances on the human subject. We will in turn deal with the substances which may be involved, the products which contain those substances, the question of dependence, the generally encountered short term (acute) effects, causes of sudden death, the likely long term (chronic) health effects, and the characteristics and dangers of some specific substances.

3.3 The volatile substances which can be misused for their drug effects are many and varied, and the spectrum of chemicals which can be employed in this way changes over time and varies geographically. The scientific and technical literature on their physiological actions and toxicological dangers is extensive, and is for the most part related to industrial exposure rather than to intentional misuse. What follows is based on the situation as we currently know it.

The substances

3.4 As already mentioned, a great many different volatile substances can be abused by inhalation. An extensive but still incomplete technical listing is given in Appendix D. In summary the most common substances currently giving rise to VSA in this country are:-

1. ALIPHATIC HYDROCARBONS, of which butane is the prime example
2. AROMATIC HYDROCARBONS, principally toluene
3. HALOGENENATED HYDROCARBONS, including 1,1,1-trichloroethane, trichloroethylene and the now largely redundant aerosol propellants (CFCs).

3.5 The commercial products which are commonly abused often contain solvent systems rather than a single substance, and even "pure" solvents may contain additives such as stabilisers and anti-oxidants which can themselves be volatile [(1) (2)]. The metabolism and toxicity of one chemical may be influenced by the presence of another [(3)], and it is possible that interactions may also occur between solvents and such common substances as aspirin [(4)], alcohol [(5) (6)], or nicotine [(7)]. Little is known about the clinical significance of any of these interactions.

The products

3.6 The kinds of product which contain abusable volatile substances are enormously extensive and widely available as household or industrial commodities. A listing of some of the commoner products together with notes on the substances which they contain is given in Appendix E. Currently, important products include adhesives, aerosols, dry-cleaning and degreasing agents, fire extinguishers, fuel gases (including cigarette lighter refills and camping gas), paints and paint thinners, paint strippers, petrol and correction material. The average household will contain many abusable products. Product characteristics have an important bearing on the mode and consequences of VSA. For instance, the butane in cigarette lighter refills is readily available to the user merely by clutching the plastic nozzle between the teeth, with the cold gas being directly inhaled with little dilution by air. In contrast toluene, which is present in contact adhesives, is contained in a viscous fluid, and when poured into a plastic bag will vaporise only slowly into the bagful of air. A consequence of these product differences and the chemical and physical differences between the actual substances shows up in the mortality statistics [(1)]. Thus butane is a common cause of immediate death probably as a result of its fast action, direct toxicity and difficulty in controlling the dose. A stimulation of the vagal nerve or the nerve endings at the back of the throat may cause vagal inhibition and slowing of the heart. Sudden, severe stimulation may result in such a profound slowing of the heart rate that it stops completely. Such a cardiac arrest may be temporary or fatal. Deaths attributed to vagal inhibition are confined to the group of abusers who spray gases which are cooled by rapid expansion (butane, aerosol propellants) into the mouth. The vapour from the less volatile and slower acting toluene, usually from glue, seems unlikely to cause sudden death, but more often gives rise to death through trauma and falls, probably because of the slow excretion and consequently more prolonged intoxication associated with this substance [(8)].

3.7 A general hazard facing the volatile substance abuser is that the drug which is being consumed is not packaged in terms of any recognisable dose as is the case with products intended for consumption, say a single cigarette, a tablet, or a half pint of beer. The user may have scant control over whether he is administering a little or a great deal of a volatile substance on any one occasion, and there can be no agreed or recognisable "standard dose". The margin of safety which defines the difference between the wanted and toxic effects can therefore rather easily be exceeded, especially so perhaps in relation to butane where the amount required to achieve intoxication is very similar to that required to cause arrhythmia. This is an irregularity in the rhythm of the heartbeat which may lead to ventricular fibrillation, when the heart does not effectively pump blood. Severe cardiac arrythmia can occur unpredictably during the abuse of any compound considered here. It is thought to be brought on by the combination of the effect of the volatile compound with stress, physical exertion or anxiety, and may lead to death within a few minutes. There is strong evidence that volatile substances induce cardiac arrhythmia directly or by potentiating the effect of adrenaline. Because death is rapid, the precise type of arrhythmia has only been recorded in a very few cases, but notably after the abuse of toluene, chlorofluorocarbons (CFCs) and butane [9] [10] [11] [12]. All in all, the dangerous dosage thresholds are unpredictable.

3.8 Further subtleties which can affect the ease of abuse of a particular product include such details as the design of the valve: butane from a cigarette lighter refill is easily abusable because the valve is an integral and accessible part of the can whereas, with camping stoves and blow torches, the accessible part of the valve is an integral part of the apparatus, not the can. Aerosols which contain a lot of propellant (deodorants or hair sprays for instance), are readily abused while products containing relatively little propellant (for example shaving foam), do not have the same ready abuse potential.

Tolerance, withdrawal, symptoms and dependence

3.9 A degree of tolerance can be induced by many of the common volatile substances which are abused, so that the experienced user will obtain a less intense response from the same degree of exposure than the naive user. Such tolerance is quickly lost if a person temporarily stops using. Experimental animal work suggests that, on cessation of continuous exposure, withdrawal symptoms may be induced with some but not all of the abusable solvents [13] [14].

3.10 The important practical questions, however, relate not so much to any dissection of the phenomena of tolerance or withdrawal, but to the holistic question of whether the taking of any of these substances can give rise to a strong drug-seeking habit, or a dependence syndrome in the clinical sense. The evidence is that, for most users, such dependence does not occur. Volatile substances are generally misused in terms of a much more intermittent dosage schedule than, say, nicotine or heroin – a matter of a few episodes a week rather than a daily or more frequent use. Furthermore, most young people who engage in VSA will, after a few months or years, break from its use with less difficulty than with many other substances, such as alcohol or tobacco.

3.11 Having stressed that VSA is typically an intermittent and non-compulsive involvement, the worrying fact remains that a small minority of users do seem to contract a more compulsive and long-term habit. There are indeed pharmacological reasons for suspecting that persistent exposure to volatile substances might be able to induce a dependence of so-called general depressant type [15].

The generally encountered effects of acute intoxication

3.12 At the physiological level, volatile substances produce intoxication through an effect on the cell membrane in a way similar to alcohol or anaesthetic gases, rather than the chemical attachment to specific cellular receptor sites. Because they are inhaled they are absorbed into the blood stream and reach the brain very quickly, so that the onset of action is rapid. The common immediate effect is one of a euphoria, confusion, unsteadiness and interference with co-ordination. Coughing, sneezing, salivation, flushing and a tendency to vomit are frequently reported. With more intense exposure intoxication becomes more marked, objects in the environment can look strange or out of perspective, and delusions and hallucinations can occur. Intoxication can progress to coma and death. Recovery from the acute effects of intoxication is usually relatively rapid unless very gross intoxication has been produced, but the rate of recovery depends on the volatility of the substance and the length of exposure.

Causes of sudden death

3.13 Volatile substance abuse is unique among drug problems in that the most common complication which brings the misuser to notice is sudden death. Such deaths may occur at first exposure or in the course of continued misuse. The causes of such tragedy can be put under two broad headings. Firstly there are those deaths which result from the direct toxic effect of the substance. Here the immediate causes can include sudden onset of abnormal heart rhythm (cardiac arrhythmia, see paragraph 3.7 above) so that the heart virtually ceases to pump blood, depression of breathing, blocking of the oxygen supply (anoxia), and a reflex stopping of the heart through a cold spray of volatile substance being taken into the mouth and stimulating the vagal nerve [8] (vaso-vagal inhibition, see paragraph 3.6 above). Whatever the underlying medical technicalities, volatile substances have the direct capacity suddenly and unpredictably to kill. Some modes of misuse can be less risky than others, but there can be no "safe" misuse. Under a second general heading can be put a variety of possible indirect causes of death such as from injuries caused by falling out of a window or drowning when intoxicated, inhalation of vomited stomach contents, asphyxia when a substance is inhaled with a plastic bag over the face, or fire or explosion when a vapour ignites [8].

Chronic physical effects

3.14 As noted in the introduction to this chapter, most of our knowledge of the possible chronic effects of volatile substances comes either from animal work or from the consequences of accidental industrial exposure. Long term studies of young people who have engaged in VSA are comparatively rare, and it cannot be assumed that the patterns, intensity and duration of use which occur with this kind of exposure will produce the same likelihood or degree of damage as the more protracted but lower dose exposures encountered in the workplace. In general, therefore, there is a scarcity of reliable information on long term damage which young people may be doing to themselves through VSA, although there is a significant number of relevant reports in the literature dealing with single cases or small series of cases which describe the toxic consequences of VSA [16] [17] [18] [19]. Without being alarmist, there are from this mixed confluence of evidence good reasons for concern. The experimental and industrial toxicological research suggests that, in some circumstances, several but not all of the commonly misused substances can cause damage to tissues of the body including the brain [20] [21], sense organs [22] [23], the peripheral nerves [24], liver [25], kidneys [26] [27] [28], and the bone marrow [29]. It is probable that, although some types of damage are recoverable, others, to a degree, will be cumulative with increased exposure and, perhaps, irreversible. Those substances which, when absorbed and metabolised, stay in the body for a long time may pose greater dangers of tissue damage than substances which are rapidly eliminated in the breath. There may be dangers to the foetus if the mother misuses volatile substances [30] [31] [32]. Prolonged exposure such as in the industrial setting may, in some instances, carry risks of cancer (carcinogenicity), and of production of genetic abnormality (mutagenicity).

Characteristics and hazards of some specific volatile substances which are currently misused

Toluene ($C_6H_5CH_3$)

3.15 Toluene is commonly found in adhesives, paints, solvents and petrol. It is a liquid with a sweet, pungent odour, produced by the chemical treatment of petroleum. Adhesives which predominantly contain toluene as the intoxicating agent have given rise to about 235 (19%) of the VSA deaths reported in the United Kingdom between 1971 and 1991. The most important acute risks are sudden death due to cardiac arrhythmia, respiratory arrest [33] and intoxication, which gives rise to death by accidental mishap. Toluene appears to be relatively slow acting with a relatively long duration of action. Chronic exposure to toluene can cause a wide variety of physical pathologies and there are reports of damage to the brain [20] [34] [35] [36] [37], although follow up studies give equivocal results as to the risk of brain damage as a sequel of VSA among school age populations [17]. The significance of such findings for VSA should not be exaggerated but there is also persuasive evidence that toluene has the capacity in some circumstances to cause damage to the eye (optic atrophy) [38], the inner ear (cochlea damage) [22], muscles [39] and peripheral nerves [24], liver [25], kidneys [28] [40] [41], lungs [42], bone marrow, heart [43] [44] and reproductive systems [45]. Toluene may also damage the foetus and there is some evidence of chromosomal damage [46].

Butane (C_4H_{10})

3.16 Butane is a gas obtained from liquid petroleum gas or the catalytic cracking of crude oil to make petrol. It is highly flammable with a lower explosive limit close to the concentration necessary to cause intoxication. Two grades of butane are likely to be encountered in VSA, one for use as a fuel and the other as an aerosol propellant, the latter being purified to remove odorous compounds. Some products contain blends of butane and the more volatile propane. Between 1971 and 1991 about 429 (34%) VSA deaths in the UK were attributable to butane from gas fuels, and an unknown but increasing proportion of the 255 (20%) deaths from aerosols will be attributable to butane.

3.17 Butane can give rise to acute fatalities both directly and indirectly [12] [47] [48]. It is fast acting with a short duration of action, necessitating repeated doses to maintain intoxication. The release of a jet of butane (or butane/propane blend) into the mouth can give rise to such intense cooling as to cause frostbite [49] and there is particular danger of a vaso-vagal response. Compared, however, to the extensive literature on the physical consequences of toluene inhalation, little data have been reported on the damage which may result from chronic exposure to butane [50]. It seems probable that dangers from this substance stem more from its properties as a simple intoxicant than from any marked capacity to inflict chronic damage on the tissues of the body. However, exposure to impurities, particularly in fuel grade butane, may have long term health consequences [51].

1,1,1 – Trichloroethane or Methylchloroform (CH_3CHCl_3)

3.18 Trichloroethane is used in some adhesives and has been employed in typewriting correction fluids, and is commonly used in industry to degrease metals. It is a liquid with a sweetish smell. Of the 142 (11%) deaths over a twenty year period from typewriter correcting fluid, plaster remover, dry cleaning fluids, domestic and industrial degreasers, many were due to trichloroethane abuse. However, it appears to pose relatively low risks of chronic tissue toxicity. Although this is one of the least toxic solvents there are well documented sudden deaths caused by cardiac sensitisation [(52)]. Manufacture of this compound will be phased out by 1996 under the Copenhagen revision of the Montreal protocol timetable on protecting the ozone layer.

Tetrachloroethylene (C_2Cl_4)

3.19 This solvent is commonly used as a dry cleaning agent in high street dry cleaning shops and in metal degreasing. It is a liquid with an aromatic smell. Some of the 44 (3%) deaths (1971-1992) from dry cleaning fluids, domestic cleaning fluids and industrial degreasers are attributable to tetrachloroethylene. There are a few reports of liver [(53)] and kidney damage [(27)] in humans but the findings are inconsistent. Chronic exposure has caused nerve damage.

Trichloroethylene ($CCl_2 = CHCl$)

3.20 Trichloroethylene ("Trike") is used as a degreasing agent and in dry cleaning (spot removal). It is a pleasant smelling liquid which was once used as an anaesthetic. It can cause death directly, and indirectly is known to cause visual disturbances and cardiac problems [(54)]. Intolerance to alcohol, manifested as a transient redness affecting the face and neck ("degreasers flush") may occur. Some of the 44 (3%) deaths (1971-1992) from dry cleaning fluids, domestic cleaning fluids and industrial degreasers are attributable to trichloroethylene.

BCF ($CBrClF_2$)

3.21 BCF (bromochlorodifluoromethane) is a liquid with a very low boiling point (a gas at ambient temperature and pressure), and it is used in fire extinguishers carried on vehicles, and for use on electrical fires. This substance is due to be phased out under the Montreal protocol to protect the ozone layer. It has over recent years enjoyed some popularity as a substance of abuse, with the majority of the 54 (4%) deaths from fire extinguishers (1971-1992) attributable to it. Little is known about its possible chronic toxicity when abused.

CFCs

3.22 The CFCs (chlorofluorocarbons) are the compounds that were once used as aerosol propellants and were principally blamed for stratospheric ozone depletion. Almost all domestic aerosols now use deodorised butane as propellant, sometimes blended with propane. Only very few specialist products, mostly medical, still contain CFCs, among which are pain relief sprays which have caused 55 (4%) deaths (1971-1992). In the short term a few products contain chlorodifluoromethane (FC 22), which is less damaging to the ozone layer, often blended with dimethyl ether.

Petrol

3.23 Petrol is a complex mixture with many different constituents which may be present in varying proportions depending on the origin of the crude oil from which it was derived. Petrol sniffing is not thought to be very widespread, with 19 (1.5%) deaths reported over 20 years. Evidence from industrial settings suggest that long term exposure to petrol fumes can cause leukaemia and various types of cancer, although the relevance of those findings to the levels and duration of exposure likely to be encountered with VSA are again very uncertain. The hexane present may cause peripheral nerve damage [(55)]. A form of acute brain inflammation (encephalopathy) may arise as a consequence of the lead compounds that are found only in leaded petrol [(56)].

Recommendations

1. The worrying and difficult paradox which arises is that we are dealing here with abusable, toxic, and potentially lethal drugs, which are at the same time the constituents of household and industrial products of enormously wide application and utility, and which will for the most part be safely used. In shaping policy, a sense of balance must be retained

2. There should be greater awareness of the true, worrying facts about danger. No VSA is without risk

CHAPTER 4

PREVENTION

Introduction

4.1 In this chapter we are concerned with what may be done to help prevent volatile substance abuse. It is probably too much to hope that prevention strategies could lead to a complete absence of volatile substance abuse (VSA) throughout the population. But at individual level there is cause to believe that young people can, given the right information and advice, decide not to start or, having started, to cease. In pursuing prevention strategies we believe that there needs to be a single, overriding, unambiguous message applicable to VSA. The message should be the theme around which all health education on VSA centres and should be used consistently by parents, carers, teachers, and all those involved in dealing with VSA.

4.2 VSA involves younger children than other forms of drug misuse except tobacco smoking. Unlike tobacco smoking, VSA can lead to sudden death. As we have already seen, such deaths are not confined to regular abusers but can and do strike first time abusers. In nearly 40% of the 122 deaths in 1991 there was no evidence of previous abuse. Each and every occasion of VSA, whether the first or the one hundredth, is a game of Russian roulette.

4.3 The young people at the receiving end of the prevention messages are younger than their counterparts experimenting with other drugs such as cannabis and ecstasy. They are using substances which seem to be inherently more dangerous. To such young people the message should be unambiguous – "VSA is too dangerous – don't do it!" This message should underpin all prevention work.

4.4 It is important then that young people should have explained to them in detail the harms coming from VSA. This should not be done in a way calculated to shock or horrify but rather to inform. Experience has shown that shocking or horrific messages can be counter-productive. They tend towards drama rather than understanding. They can leave young people with an enduring feeling of excitement rather than understanding.

4.5 The aim should be to leave young people with an understanding that they should not misuse these substances because they are just too dangerous. They will therefore need a clear appreciation of the detailed dangers which lie behind VSA. (Such appreciation will allow continuation of the difficult task of keeping up a dialogue with those who, despite warnings, will go on to misuse volatile substances, matters which we come to below.)

4.6 It would be naive to think that merely warning young people will necessarily stop them from abusing. Education and counselling needs to take account of the audience to whom it is addressed. Thus a simple "it's too dangerous – don't do it" message may be sufficient for younger children and there will be sense in it for older children too. But in older children it would be a mistake to use the message unheedingly without taking account of their skills and experience. Thus the message should offer a perspective from which to initiate discussion, which should be developed according to the age, setting, skills and experience of the young people involved, with the aim of helping them make healthy, informed choices. The more worldly the participants the greater will be the need to discuss the harms which follow from particular methods, techniques and situations of abuse. For example, in a one-to-one setting with a confirmed abuser it will be more appropriate to discuss ways of avoiding the more harmful forms of VSA than it would be with a young group. We explore below the risks involved in VSA and how we feel discussion of them should be approached.

Types of risk

Substance specific risks

4.7 There has been debate about the harm which can come from butane and other gases and aerosols as opposed to the toluene based glues. Previously some workers have recommended that young sniffers should use glues rather than aerosols and gases. The scientific basis for such a distinction is questionable, and we do not believe that there should ever be the positive recommendation of so called 'safer sniffing'. Such recommendations would confuse and undermine our strong "it's too dangerous – don't do it" message.

4.8 However, this leaves open the question as to whether one can identify any substances which are the "most dangerous". On the basis of evidence we have heard, we do not think there is a case for such a strategy. The evidence for different levels of harm for different substances is too weak to justify such an identification of greatest harm from specific substances. We are aware that what is being said here is a departure from the message on VSA which some people have previously been using.

Technique specific risks

4.9 There have been cases of suffocation when young sniffers have put their heads inside large plastic bags to concentrate the fumes. Knowledge of this has led some health educators to argue that advice should be given to sniffers to use smaller bags. Whilst we understand the good intentions of those making such suggestions we do not think that a message in such terms is helpful. As we have said above, workers and adults generally should not put themselves in a position of arguing for 'safe sniffing'. It is a contradiction in terms.

4.10 However, given the deaths which have occurred from the use of plastic bags in this way it would in our view be irresponsible for teachers and other professionals not to point out in robust terms to young people the exceptional hazards involved in this practice. Fudging this issue because of the difficulty in delivering the general message could lead to unnecessary ignorance and consequential harm. Standing on the sidelines and saying that it is their own fault – they should have heeded our warnings not to use volatile substances at all – is clearly inadequate.

4.11 A well documented technique which carries an exceptional risk of death is that of spraying the contents of aerosols and gases, most notably cigarette lighter refills, direct into the mouth and throat. Given the deaths from this practice it would again be wrong not to spell out carefully this specific exceptional hazard for young people, while again not implying that VSA can ever be safe.

4.12 Another technique-specific hazard is that of having lighted cigarettes in the vicinity whilst sniffing a volatile substance. The risk here is that of setting fire to the solvents or perhaps the clothing of the sniffer, or causing an explosion. The degrees of hazard depends on the technique and substance sniffed. Thus the presence of a lighted cigarette whilst sniffing butane and crouched under a cover to trap the fumes is probably the most dangerous practice one can imagine. There have been cases of serious burns and fatalities resulting from such reckless activity.

Situation specific risks

4.13 There are also risks arising from intoxication in dangerous places. There have been drownings of sniffers who were intoxicated on canal and river banks. And there have been accidents to those who have gone onto railway embankments or who have sniffed near busy roads.

4.14 Some workers have in the past advised sniffing in safer venues. Once more we feel it necessary strongly to argue against such advice which, in our view, goes too far. But, given the deaths which we have described from situational hazards, it is equally clear that we must include these risks in the detailed advice to some young people.

Parents and carers

4.15 The involvement and support of parents and carers is an important factor in drug education to ensure that parents, carers and schools convey essentially the same messages. Our recommendations in our previous report, "Drug Education in Schools: the Need for a New Impetus" (1), encouraged parents' involvement in schools' education programmes.

4.16 But the parents and carers themselves need to know something of the dangers of VSA and to know what to do, or whom to contact for help or advice. There are, in fact, a number of organisations which can provide information on VSA. For example, Re-Solv, the Society for the Prevention of Solvent and Volatile Substance Abuse, is a charity solely concerned with VSA. There are also others but what is important is that parents and carers should know that there are places to which they can turn and what those places are. Appendix F contains some suggestions of useful contacts.

4.17 Gaining this knowledge is part and parcel of the need to heighten awareness, on which some progress has already been made. For example, the Department of Health produced in 1992 a leaflet, "Solvents – A Parent's Guide" (2) (see paragraph 1.26). Subsequently in January 1994, following a pilot campaign which compared distribution strategies in four different parts of the country, the Health Departments launched a three month television and press campaign aimed at parents encouraging them to discuss drugs and solvents with their children, which promoted a leaflet "Drugs and Solvents – you and your child" (3). We understand that over 2.25 million copies have been issued and that it has been translated into 10 ethnic minority languages. The Department of Health has also brought out new leaflets or re-issued existing ones, namely:

> "Drugs and Solvents – things you should know" (4) for 13-18 year olds
>
> "Drugs and Solvents – a young person's guide" (5) for 8-12 year olds
>
> "Drug and Solvent Misuse – a basic briefing" (6) for professionals, parents and others who need to know more about drugs and their effects.

We acknowledge and welcome this work. A brief summary of the evaluation of the parents campaign is contained in paragraphs 4.46 and 4.47.

School-based education

4.18 In our report "Drug Education in Schools: the Need for New Impetus" we concluded that there was a consensus that drug education is more likely to be effective when it is sustained and intensive, and more likely to have an impact when it teaches decision-making and life-skills rather than relying on a didactic approach. The recommendations of that report were based on those principles. As we have made clear elsewhere in the present report, we are of the view that VSA should form part of any drug education programme and indeed, in our previous report, we specifically included volatile substances among the drugs about which children, parents and teachers should be educated.

Community action

4.19 Approaches to prevention, other than those of providing information and promoting schools-based education, can also be adopted locally. The local teams of the Home Office Drugs Prevention Initiative, who have been working with local people in 20 areas of the country to develop community-based responses to drug misuse, have broadly identified five approaches: information and awareness-raising; education and training; diversionary alternatives; stimulating and supporting community development; and criminal justice drugs interventions. These different approaches are interdependent. For instance, a programme of diversionary activities for young people at risk in a given area may need to be co-ordinated with a local information campaign aimed at that age group to enhance the prospects of success. Common to each of the approaches is the importance of tailoring them precisely to meet the needs, situations and perceptions of local people; of involving local people in devising the solutions to the problems which they themselves have identified; and of different local agencies working together in partnership.

4.20 Some of the local drugs prevention teams have supported work aimed specifically at preventing VSA. Examples include:

- the Brighton and Hove team funded the development of comics with the minimum use of words by a Personal Social and Health Education Advisory Teacher, thus providing information about VSA for young people with low and no reading ability. In the light of evaluation of a pilot comic on glue-sniffing in 1992, three on solvents, cannabis and ecstasy were produced in 1993. The team also supported a Community Networking project relating to VSA, with the object of providing training for community workers through multi-agency workshops.

- in Salford, the team has since 1992 supported a local campaign, "Parents Against the Use of Lethal Substances", which has promoted a drama produced by and involving young people themselves, as well as a "Danger of Butane in Aerosols" display stand which has been put up in various venues across the city.

- the Nottingham team has supported Open Doors, a small drugs prevention project working with young people in Nottingham which started out as a self-help group for those involved in VSA. The team's support has helped the project to broaden its remit from VSA to misuse of other drugs as well as addressing young people's involvement in offending and other social and personal concerns.

- the Birmingham team is supporting a programme of work aimed at informing children of primary-school age about VSA. "Jimmy Sniffs and Very Safe Anni" involves a three book teaching pack on VSA, and a theatre in education performance which uses songs and poems to communicate personal safety messages to the children.

4.21 The Drugs Prevention Initiative is currently engaged in a collective programme of work aimed at pulling together lessons learned from local achievement and experience. Much of the information gathered about what works should apply also to VSA. Good practice guidance should, we understand, begin to be made available in the first half of 1995.

Vulnerable groups

4.22 In terms of prevention there is considerable attraction in the idea of targeting those youngsters who seem most likely to abuse volatile substances. Regrettably, as is brought out in Chapter 2, there is a range of predisposing factors and we suggest that it is not possible on present knowledge with any reasonable degree of accuracy to target particular groups on the basis of their circumstances. Accordingly we conclude that prevention needs to be aimed at all youngsters. If all youngsters are to be covered it must not be forgotten that not all children are at school.

4.23 In Chapter 2 we highlighted the fact that children who are looked after by the local authority, who may be accommodated in residential homes or foster homes, may be particularly vulnerable to VSA. It is important that those who are looking after children and young people in care are vigilant to the possibility of VSA. If misuse is identified it would be counter-productive to adopt a punitive approach. Part of the child's care plan should include a multi-agency approach to prevention, assessment and treatment. It is important that the response to VSA is part of the total care package for the child or young person and not seen as a separate, stigmatising piece of work.

Control of supply

4.24 So far in this chapter we have been discussing measures which would help to reduce demand for abusable volatile substances. We believe there are also approaches, short of legislation (the amendment of which we do not recommend – see paragraph 1.28), which would help to reduce the supply side of the equation.

4.25 The volatile substances which can be abused to achieve intoxication in the United Kingdom have all been produced for legitimate purposes. Their efficacy when used properly, and the reliance which society puts on them, makes total withdrawal unrealistic. Whenever potentially abusable products are used for their proper purposes they should be handled responsibly.

4.26 In the home it is obviously not reasonable to suppose that all abusable substances can be made totally inaccessible. They are too plentiful and include products such as aerosol sprays, cigarette lighter refills and solvent-based glues. We would not suggest that all these items should be kept under lock and key. But parents and carers need to be aware of what these substances are; their potential for abuse; and, when the products are used for their proper purpose, to encourage children to treat them responsibly. We would hope that, through enhanced awareness, parents and carers would consider keeping some products out of reach and be alert to signs of possible VSA. Thus just as they might keep alcoholic drinks shut away or question the reasons for empty cans or bottles, they might think about the possibility of VSA if they find, for example, empty butane, aerosol or glue cans, or plastic bags in places where their child has been. No parent wants to be constantly prying, but informed alertness is the basis of safeguard.

4.27 Outside the home, commercial and industrial premises, building sites, offices and schools can provide a source of intoxicants (for example, butane and propane) for the volatile substance abuser. He or she may gain access to these either through forced entry or through negligence of the owners leaving unsecured premises where such substances are held. Such opportunities for abusers should be kept to an absolute minimum. Local authorities might encourage contractors not to leave abusable substances lying around on building sites.

Retailers

4.28 Under the Intoxicating Substances (Supply) Act 1985, and under common law in Scotland, retailers commit an offence if they supply an intoxicating substance if they believe that it may be abused by a person under eighteen. It is important therefore that retailers are familiar with the products which are liable to abuse. Our recommendations on product labelling and wholesale package labelling (see paragraphs 4.37 to 4.44) would help to achieve this aim. But there is more that could and should be done. Training of retailers and their staff can help them identify the abusable products and the possible abusers. They will then be able to make judgements about where products should be displayed, if at all, and to whom it might be unwise to sell. They will also need to prevent theft of these products.

4.29 To help focus this important training work we would like to suggest the following objectives for all staff working in retail settings with abusable substances:

- staff should know in general terms about VSA and that it involves the deliberate inhalation of a wide range of volatile substances;
- they should be able to identify all the abusable substances on sale in their retail setting;
- they should be able to distinguish between abusable and non-abusable versions of similar products (for example, solvent- and water- based adhesives);
- they should know their legal responsibilities on VSA;
- they should know who to contact locally for additional information.

4.30 In considering the range of training, attention needs to be paid to the ethnic make up of retailers. There are some for whom English may not be their first language. Also, the extent of any VSA problem in minority communities is not known. Thus there is a need for advice leaflets to be available in languages other than English and a particular need to ensure that the problem in the community as a whole is appreciated.

4.31 There is a temptation to regard all retailers as independent isolated units when in fact many are covered by trade associations. We suggest that these trade associations have a responsibility in getting the VSA message to retailers.

4.32 In putting forward these proposals on retailers we are conscious that much good work has been done already, whether with trade association assistance or not. Many retailers have become more cautious about marketing abusable products and this is to be welcomed. But it remains important that their guard should not drop and that retailers who have not yet acted against potential VSA should do so.

Product design and modification

4.33 The best time to consider the safety issues of a product is in the design stage - modification of an existing product is nearly always more difficult. In considering the introduction of new products we urge manufacturers to consider how to keep volatile substance abuse potential to a minimum. There are a number of ways in which abuse potential might be reduced whether in relation to new products or through modifying existing products. First, in some cases it may be possible to replace or reduce the abusable volatile element of the product with a non-abusable alternative. Second, substances might be added to give it a nasty taste – we understand that manufacturers concentrate on taste rather than smell since a product with an unpleasant smell is likely to put off legitimate users. Third, the way the product is delivered from its container might be re-designed so as to make abuse less easy. In considering modification there is a need to ensure that the result is not a product which is more hazardous in normal use.

4.34 Manufacturers are, of course, subject to market pressures and will be keen to retain their market share. However with their social responsibilities in mind we would expect manufacturers who know their products are abusable to be interested in product design and modification. We know of manufacturers who are interested and continue to look at ways of making their products less liable to volatile substance abuse. We commend such action.

4.35 The Montreal Convention and subsequent European Community (EC) regulations impose controls on the production and supply of ozone depleting substances. Manufacturers will, as a result, be required to phase out the use of a number of chemicals over the next few years. The effect of this is that manufacturers are having to re-examine those products which contain these chemicals. Since they are having to do so for this reason it would appear to provide an opportunity to consider the products' abuse potential. In the process of re-examination we would urge manufacturers to consider the abuse potential and toxicity of possible substitutes, and to reduce both so far as possible. The mechanism through which to achieve the aim described in the preceding three paragraphs might be the body whose establishment we recommend in paragraph 4.44.

4.36 There is one specific area where we believe the level of abuse and danger is such that the product should be modified. As we said in paragraph 3.6, butane from cigarette lighter refills is readily abusable and is a common cause of immediate death, probably as a result of its fast action, direct toxicity and difficulty in controlling dose. These refills are available in sizes which enable large and consequently dangerous amounts to be inhaled. We believe the dangers could be reduced by limiting the maximum size of cigarette lighter refills to 25ml, and we therefore recommend such a limitation in size.

Product labelling

4.37 In looking at the desirability of putting warning labels on products which are abusable we take the view that it is necessary to consider who will read them. We have identified three principal groups: parents and carers, children, and shopkeepers.

4.38 To help shopkeepers we see a strong argument for wholesalers including on their packaging a message for products which are abusable. This would alert shopkeepers to the risk associated with some products they stock, and assist in ensuring that they did not contravene the Intoxicating Substances (Supply) Act 1985 or Scottish common law. The shopkeeper would also be able to make informed decisions about where he might most safely keep or display these products.

4.39 We believe parents and carers should be provided with a warning about products which are abusable by inhalation. At a general level it would help to raise the level of awareness and ensure that the subject stayed in the public eye. In the home, parents would be able to identify easily those products which they should have concerns about if, for example, they go missing or appear to be being used up more quickly than usual. Our preference would be to see a simple message developed for a label, such as "this product is safe if properly used but is capable of misuse if deliberately inhaled".

4.40 A label designed for parents and carers would inevitably be read by children as well. A fear which has been expressed is that such a label would alert children to new products which they might abuse rather than have the intended effect of discouragement. While recognising this view we feel that in practice it is unlikely that abusers would learn anything which they did not already know, and we believe that, on balance, the advantages outweigh any possible disadvantages.

4.41 How should labelling be achieved? We have been advised that the introduction of legislation in the UK would contravene EC obligations. But we do not regard this as fatal to our proposals on labelling.

4.42 There are already examples where industry has voluntarily labelled some products which are liable to abuse. We believe that these should be encouraged and built upon. Our feeling is that industry should regulate itself and decide what its strategy for labelling should be and then introduce standards which all producers should adopt. The agreement would be voluntary but we would hope that all producers would take part. As and when labelling comes into effect research should be undertaken to establish its impact.

4.43 In summary, therefore, we believe that labelling would be in the public interest and that industry should introduce its own self-regulatory regime.

4.44 In the preceding paragraphs we have discussed ways in which we believe that producers could make their products less liable to misuse, whether in terms of the substances themselves or the vehicle of administration. We have also made suggestions for product labelling. To ensure that the aims we have described are furthered we recommend the establishment of a standing forum representing industry, and industry-led, for the sharing of ideas and experience. We envisage senior levels of industry being able to meet, perhaps with representatives from Re-Solv and the expert medical advisory field, to consider the misuse potential of their products and how to reduce it. The forum could not have legal powers, but it would need to be influential and to be able to act as a broker between health and industrial interests. The setting up of such a body would require the stimulation of Government.

Public awareness

4.45 We have mentioned in various parts of this chapter the need to heighten awareness of VSA as a problem. There are those who will argue that such a course will only serve to encourage potential abusers but, as we have said earlier, we believe the advantages exceed the disadvantages. Our view is that informed media coverage on the subject is to be welcomed. There are examples of national, regional and local campaigns which have had impact. The media have an important part to play in influencing the social agenda which could and should be used to trigger action at local level for dealing with VSA.

4.46 In paragraph 4.17 we mentioned the Government's 1994 national three month campaign on VSA aimed at parents, which included television advertising. The evaluation of the campaign showed:

- a slight increase in awareness by parents that drug misuse and VSA could be an issue for them and their children;
- a slight increase in awareness that peer group pressure could be an important factor;
- evidence that parents felt better informed and better placed to talk to their children.

Among those who had discussions with their children, the television advertising was found to have been a significant prompt to constructive dialogue. Knowledge of Department of Health leaflets was found to have increased from a 1992 level of 25% to 39% and possession of the item to have increased from 4% to 15% in the same period. Possession of leaflets made parents feel better informed and more confident in discussing the subject with their children and made them more likely to have done so.

4.47 The Department of Health acknowledges that the changes were slight but point to evidence that most successful social persuasion advertising, such as the drink-drive campaign, works in this way. The VSA mortality data for 1992 shows that the number of deaths dipped in the months following the campaign [(7)]. If it is the case that the fall in deaths was contributed to by the campaign, then this is very welcome, but we would caution against over-interpretation.

Recommendations

1. Prevention must be both person and community focused, and product focused

2. The fundamental and consistent message which we advocate for all health statements on this topic made to young people as individuals or to wider target audiences is the unambiguous – "VSA is too dangerous, don't do it" (4.2 – 4.3)

3. With some committed users no advice is likely to bring immediate cessation. Without accidentally conveying the misleading and dangerous message that any form of VSA can be safe, it is legitimate with such users to suggest strategies which may reduce danger (4.6)

4. Education on VSA needs tailoring to the particular circumstances of those in the educational group. The general "VSA is too dangerous – don't do it" message should not be used heedlessly or as a slogan but as the

invariable basis of any discussions which explore VSA and how to avoid its more dangerous forms. The aim should be to help young people make healthy, informed decisions (4.6)

5. School based education on VSA should be integrated with drug education and teach decision making and life skills within the model previously proposed in the ACMD report on Drug Education in Schools (4.15 – 4.18)

6. Parents and carers should take sensible safeguards in the home, and potentially abusable substances should be responsibly handled wherever they are used. Trade associations have a responsibility in getting a VSA prevention message to retailers (4.26 and 4.31)

7. A variety of approaches to product design and modification can help to make potentially abusable substances less easy to administer or less attractive (4.33 – 4.35)

8. We are particularly worried about the sale of cigarette lighter refills in sizes which give ready access to dangerous amounts of butane. We recommend that the size of such refills should be limited to 25 ml (4.36)

9. On product labelling, we firstly recommend that wholesalers should include on their packaging a message to identify products which are liable to abuse, and hence alert shopkeepers to risk. Secondly, we recommend that parents should be provided with warnings about products liable to abuse with labels of appropriate size and clarity. Such labelling can only be introduced on a voluntary basis (4.37 – 4.43)

10. We strongly recommended the establishment of an industry-led forum, perhaps with representatives from Re-Solv and others, to share ideas and experience and secure relevant action. This initiative should be stimulated by Government (4.44)

11. Much of what we say is based on our assessment that there is a need to heighten public awareness of VSA in order that its prevention receives the attention which it deserves (4.45 – 4.47)

CHAPTER 5

STRENGTHENING COMMUNITY-BASED HELP FOR VOLATILE SUBSTANCE MISUSERS AND THEIR FAMILIES

The scope of this chapter

5.1 The central argument of this chapter is that strengthened help for volatile substance misusers and their families must be rooted in existing community resources. To that end we offer here some guidelines and a framework for action. The discussion is, however, purposely not taken to a great level of detail and will avoid being over-prescriptive – the design and implementation of local responses to local problems can properly only be determined locally.

5.2 In paragraph 5.4 a set of general principles are outlined which relate to how help is to be made better available. Paragraphs 5.5 – 5.15 deal with help for volatile substance misusers, while paragraphs 5.16 – 5.17 consider the needs of families.

5.3 Although the focus of this chapter is on treatment, that question borders closely on prevention (chapter 4), training (chapter 6) and planning (chapter 7). Much of the local organisational structure required for the co-ordination and strengthening of treatment will overlap or even be identical with the required organisational basis for prevention, planning and training. To avoid duplication, chapter 6 will therefore take this broader focus and consider the overall mechanisms needed for an integrated community response to volatile substance abuse (VSA).

Availability of support – general principles

5.4 Much good work is already being done in many parts of this country to help volatile substance abusers and their families, and there is valuable experience on which to build. It would though be going too far to suppose that, on a countrywide basis, help for VSA is available on a scale which matches the problem, or with a degree of flexibility to match the many different needs and presentations. When identifying strategies to strengthen the existing responses, action will need to be guided by the following general considerations.

- **Different localities will be experiencing different levels of problem occurrence.** Services must be sensitive to the fact that VSA is a national problem with uneven geographical distribution and that prevalence may vary steeply over time, with sudden, unexpected, outbreaks. Planning of the needed responses is therefore inevitably a task which must be accomplished at a local level. It is possible that perceived sudden unexpected outbreaks of VSA are sometimes little more than a manifestation of media interest. Services might therefore consider drawing up contingency plans for rapid responses to media interest.
- **VSA is, for the individual, a problem which can exist in different degrees and with varying persistence.** Help is required for the casual, experimental user, as well as for the person who has become entrenched in prolonged and heavy use of volatile substances.
- **Behind the differing use patterns lies a varied population of users with varying needs.** This variety can exist along several dimensions which include age and gender, aspects of self-image, personal integration and happiness, and psychological well-being. The great majority of users are likely to be otherwise healthy and well adjusted, but some may be showing multiple behavioural problems, while a small minority will be experiencing severe psychological problems which will require attention in their own right. The pattern of available services must reflect and be responsive to this personal variation.
- **Varied life situations.** Help must not only be responsive to the user as an individual, but must reach users who are experiencing very different life situations – those who are still at school or who have left school, persistent truants or steady school attenders, those who have the advantage of a supportive and intact home and those who are looked after by the local

authority, and perhaps accommodated in residential care or with foster parents, the privileged and the deprived. The needed help will usually have a social as well as a psychological element.

Volatile substances may be the individual's only substance problem, or one of several. VSA may be the only substance problem which the individual is experiencing, or it may be accompanied by misuse of alcohol or other dugs. It may be one phase in what later proves to be a multiple and sequential drug using career. More frequently, once VSA is out of the way, the individual will have no further misuse problems.

Family issues. Most young people who use volatile substances will be of an age where they will still be living with their family. VSA is therefore often a family problem. Help for parents and other family members may be an essential but indirect component in helping the user, or the family may in its own right need support in dealing with what is felt as threat or crisis.

Generalists and specialists. By far the greatest proportion of the needed individual and family help will be delivered by family doctors, teachers, youth workers and general social and community agencies, including social workers. Workers or agencies with a specialist knowledge of VSA are needed in support of these vital, general, activities.

Co-ordination. In that the needed help will, within any one locality, be provided by many different agencies, a mechanism for co-ordination will be an important part of any overall, planned response.

A central treatment goal, but the possibility of many important intermediate or accompanying goals. The strategy which we suggest is based on the belief that the central treatment goal in this area is to help the individual to stop sniffing. With this type of substance problem, the dangers of sudden death are so unpredictable that it is not responsible to suggest "safer use" as a goal. At the same time it would be naive to ignore the reality that many users will not stop at the first helping contact. Agencies will often be working productively with young people who are still using volatile substances, regularly or intermittently. In this period, as we said earlier, we believe that for those who do not give up there is a case to be made for advising them away from the most risky methods of abuse. With chronic abusers there might also be useful intermediate goals which can be adopted. These might, for instance, relate to their psychological needs, social circumstances, family understanding, or getting back into education. They might also include reducing the frequency of use as a step towards complete abstention.

Help for the individual who is misusing volatile substances

5.5 So far as we are aware, there have not been any controlled trials or other formal evaluations conducted in this country on the treatment of VSA. The approaches outlined in this section are therefore based on an appraisal of current good practice. Given the emphasis which we have already put on the varied nature of the problem, it must be evident that "good practice" will constitute a layered series of alternative or multiple strategies rather than any one master stroke.

Simple advice and sympathetic dialogue

5.6 With VSA, as with so many other problems, simple advice, given in a straightforward and unhectoring way, and in terms intelligible to a young person, is the basic ingredient of all types of relevant help. There is an important distinction between advice confidently and sensibly given and which is likely to carry credibility, and preachy or scaremongering pronouncements which are only likely to alienate the user and lose the informant his credibility. The aim of advice is to enable the individual to make an informed and healthy personal choice.

5.7 There may be occasions when what is being sought by a user is, simply, information directly on volatile substances. A query about volatile substances is, though, more likely to be an opening for listening to that young person's own perceptions and misunderstandings relating to VSA, with the focus of discussion perhaps then broadening from VSA to personal issues and life context.

5.8 Advice and dialogue as a basic component of treatment is continuous with the same strategies as prevention. The target population for this kind of interaction therefore embraces the non-user who needs to be helped not to experiment, the occasional user who needs to be helped to stop before going further, and also the person who is engaging in more persistent use and who may need formal help in addition to the relatively low-key kind of response we are describing here.

5.9 The provision of adequate community-wide help of this type depends on a wide range of people having the skills, knowledge, commitment and confidence to interact with young people in relation to VSA. Far from dismissing this level of response as trivial or obvious we believe that it is the capacity for this kind of community reaction to VSA which must in particular be strengthened. The fact-givers need to know the facts better so as to have the capacity to engage in useful, open, dialogue. The range of agents and agencies who can valuably contribute to this basic level of response include teachers and more widely the school as community; youth workers; churches and religious groups; statutory and non-statutory social agencies; general practitioners and the primary health care team; the police; parents, friends and neighbours. A park-keeper or the caretaker in a block of flats can be, if informed and empowered, part of the local community resource for responding to VSA.

5.10 Much of what is being said here could again equally apply to any other type of social problem, and certainly to problems set by the use of alcohol and other drugs by young people. The ability of a community to respond more effectively to the specific problem of VSA does though crucially depend on those concerned having the requisite knowledge available to them, and having an enhanced awareness of VSA as an issue.

More intensive help for the individual

5.11 For more persistent VSA or for misuse which is occurring against the background of wider life difficulties or in the context of multiple behaviour problems, help may be needed which still employs advice and dialogue as a basic element but which in addition offers more intensive or wider help. Here, also, what has to be envisaged is a graded and flexible deployment of help rather than any standard package.

5.12 Individual counselling may be based on any one of many different models, but is likely to explore some or all of the following issues:

- the causes of VSA and practical ways of avoiding the triggering of use;
- the identification of healthy and rewarding alternative activities;
- peer group and family relationships;
- self-image and self-assertiveness;
- health and respect for self.

5.13 Experimental approaches for persistent VSA have sometimes supplemented counselling with activity programmes at a local base, or as offered through adventure training and weeks away. The attempt can then also be made to harness therapeutically the power of the group. Misusers who have felt marginalised need, furthermore, to be helped back into rewarding contact with their own communities. There has been some limited experience with the setting up of "Glue Anon" or Alcoholics Anonymous types of self-help group, but it is difficult to envisage this type of organisation being widely replicated without a great deal of facilitation, given the usual age range of VSA.

5.14 A minority of volatile substance misusers may at some point require residential help which can provide a respite and allow new directions to be identified and agreed. The National Children's Bureau has a database of agencies that will provide that kind of residential care for young people who are engaging in VSA or other types of drug misuse.

5.15 As for the kinds of agency which can contribute to the level of help outlined in this section, in some localities there may be agencies or individual workers who have special expertise with VSA and who are working within the voluntary or statutory sectors. Re-Solv, a national agency listed in Appendix F, may be able to give information on such local resources. The specialist contributions to this level of help are in particular likely at present to come from youth workers and youth projects; the probation service; intermediate treatment projects; workers in night shelters and others who provide care for the homeless; social workers; voluntary street drug agencies; outreach workers; detached workers; and Child Mental Health clinics. NHS Community Drug Teams (CDTs) will often be dealing with VSA in passing and will occasionally encounter young adults for whom VSA is a continuing, major, or even central problem, but the CDTs' age spectrum is in general significantly older than the age band within which VSA predominantly falls.

Help for families

5.16 As with the types of help needed for the individual misuser so, with the family, the emphasis should be on ensuring that a flexible range of help is available with the larger need being for simple, accessible, community-based assistance rather than for specialist or intensive interventions. When VSA comes to light in a family it will often confront the parents with a sense of fright and confusion. They may be uncertain how to react and what to say. Again what is therefore most needed is a friendly, experienced and listening ear, and someone who can give basic information and informed reassurance. This type of help may come from the school or from a parents group, from the general practitioner or primary health care team, or from many other community resources, including those mentioned in paragraph 5.15. It should, though, be admitted that finding a ready way to the right kind of first-level help when a family is confronted by VSA is not always easy in all parts of the country. There are again gaps in service and gaps in knowledge which need to be filled.

5.17 More specialised or intensive family work may be needed when VSA is in effect flagging up the fact that a family is otherwise deeply under stress or having difficulty in functioning as a family group. Such help may be provided by a variety of the generic family resources available in the community. Types of help may include groups in which a number of families come together for support, or some kind of family therapy.

Recommendations

1. **A strategy to provide strengthened help for volatile substance misusers and their families must be developed within a framework which builds on existing and largely generic community resources, and which recognises that the pattern of local responses to local problems must be locally determined. We identify the main features which characterise such a framework** (5.1 and 5.4)

2. **The basis for all types of help given to the volatile substance misuser must be simple and informed advice, and the ability to enter into sympathetic dialogue** (5.6 - 5.10)

3. **A flexible range of support and assistance will also be needed for families** (5.16 – 5.17)

CHAPTER 6

TRAINING

Introduction

6.1 In 1990 we produced a report on training which made recommendations designed to improve the range, quantity and quality of drug misuse training [(1)]. Many of these recommendations hold good for training on volatile substance issues. The most relevant of these are repeated in this chapter.

Who needs training and about what?

- Educationalists need training as drug educators of young people. These include teachers, youth workers, those working in intermediate treatment and other social work or probation staff involved in educational work with young people.

- Educationalists need training in their pastoral role, coping with young people who may be misusing volatile substances or with volatile substance abuse (VSA) related incidents in educational settings such as schools and youth clubs.

- Staff in a wide range of caring and treating professions need further in-service education to help them work with volatile substance abusers.

- Specialist drug treatment and advice staff need to keep up to date with current trends in VSA and need help to develop their skills in working with this client group.

- Parents should have access to information/education sessions (possibly through Parent-Teacher Associations).

Educationalists in their educational role

6.2 These staff need to know about the nature of VSA, patterns of use, and the hazards associated with it. They need to understand the principles of education about drugs, and possess the skills and confidence effectively to deliver such education. These issues were covered in our recent report on drug education in schools [(2)].

6.3 From an educational perspective VSA can best be seen as another aspect of drug misuse which should be dealt with in the context of a broad approach to health and social education. In our schools report we proposed an aim for drug education of "enabling pupils to make healthy informed choices".

6.4 We went on to set objectives for drug education of increasing knowledge, changing attitudes, and enhancing skills; changing behaviour; and promoting responsible citizenship. Under each of these headings we set more detailed objectives. All of these apply equally in the educational response to VSA.

6.5 We also made recommendations in our schools report about the context within which the education should take place. This took account of age, sex, community and cultural contexts of the individuals and schools concerned. We went on to make recommendations on the content, methods and organisation within the school of drug education. Again, all of these recommendations hold good for education about VSA.

6.6 To help teachers, school nurses and others to achieve these objectives we made some recommendations on their training needs which are worth reiterating here.

> *Initial training*
>
> "10.12 There is a need for recognised courses and consistent national standards of provisions of training at initial training level. Minimal training expectations should be defined, mechanisms should be put in

place to ensure that such training is made available and the prestige of such work should be enhanced and related to career prospects. Training provision should be reviewed and monitored periodically."

In service training

"10.13 .... there is a need for co-ordinated approach which sets national standards and minimal training expectations and which sets up mechanisms for ensuring that in-service training is provided and monitored. All the schools, both primary and secondary, should have a trained co-ordinator who can take a lead role in delivering drug education to children and in enhancing the skills of other teachers across the school. There is merit in opening in-service courses for teachers to others who play a part in the drug education programme such as police officers."

6.7 The recommendations applied and continue to apply equally to volatile substances. Given the involvement in educational activities of staff in youth services, social services and other disciplines, it would also be appropriate to open up such in-service courses to these staff.

Educationalists in their pastoral role

6.8 As VSA is predominantly a teenage phenomenon it is often encountered within educational settings as a policy, practical and pastoral problem. Teachers, school caretakers, youth workers, residential social workers and others working in educational settings therefore need training in a variety of coping skills appropriate to these contexts. They need training in the following areas:

understanding patterns of young people's VSA both locally and nationally;

assessment skills to enable them to respond appropriately to different levels of misuse;

- basic first aid skills to help them cope with intoxication and collapse;
- skills in communicating with young people who may be in distress or resistant to explanation of their VSA;
- issues relating to confidentiality – when to inform parents or other authorities and so on;
- the application of rules and punishments to volatile substance misusing behaviour;
- the law relating to VSA and the roles of the police in relation to misusers;
- the range and function of support agencies who can help with volatile substance misusers;
- the development of appropriate policies to manage VSA;
- consideration of the boundaries of this expertise and at what point to refer to outside professional guidance and support.

Staff in a wide range of caring and treating professions

6.9 Staff in services such as probation, the police, social work in field work and day care settings, community nursing, accident and emergency units, general practitioners and pharmacists will come across volatile substance misusers in a wide variety of settings. Their basic training should have equipped them to deal with the specific professional issues which lead them to encounter the misuser. Thus a probation officer or social worker coming across a young offender who is also a volatile substance misuser should be skilled in dealing with young people as such.

6.10 Despite this basic training there is a need for all these disciplines to understand the nature and complexity of VSA, together with its associated hazards. These disciplines will need to master many of the specific issues noted in paragraph 6.8 above together with an understanding of how these relate to their own particular work contexts.

Specialist drug treatment and advice staff

6.11 Staff working in specialist agencies who deal with a range of substance users will need training in VSA issues. They will often be the source of specialist advice to teachers and others, even if they are not always working with the young volatile substance misusers directly.

6.12 There is a need to ensure that the specialists are indeed specialists in volatile substance issues as well as on other drug matters. They will need regular updates on the changing VSA scene and access to the latest scientific evidence on the nature and consequences of VSA. Given their role as a local source of expertise, it is particularly important that they are kept well briefed.

6.13 Staff of drug agencies, many of whom are trained and experienced in working exclusively with adult drug users, may need, through additional training and education, to develop their expertise in working with young people (and their parents and carers) who are misusing volatile substances or other drugs.

How should the training be delivered?

Basic level and qualifying training

6.14 In our previous report on training we argued that all staff likely to encounter drug users should have been provided with a basic level understanding of drugs in their qualifying level training. We recommended

> "...that each validating body should give priority to determining the basic levels of drug related knowledge, skills and understanding appropriate to their professions". (p21)

6.15 This recommendation is as relevant today as it was then, although we would now explicitly want to extend it to cover VSA as well.

6.16 Over the last few years there has been a major change in the delivery systems of professional training within the UK. Competency based training now dominates new training development in many disciplines. National and Scottish Vocation Qualifications (N/SVQs) are being developed and will create a system for measuring levels of competence in practice. A number of N/SVQs have already been established for care workers in criminal justice and more generally in social work.

6.17 Within the Level 3 Care N/SVQ a substance abuse option or "endorsement" is currently under development, and is being consulted upon as this report is being written. There is as yet no reference to VSA in the units which will comprise this endorsement. Neither as we understand it, is any consideration being given within the N/SVQ systems to developing the competency of youth and community workers in relation to drug and volatile substance misusers. We believe this to be unfortunate and recommend that the relevant lead bodies give this their immediate attention.

In-service and multi-disciplinary training and education

6.18 For those staff who may not yet have been trained on VSA issues, in-service training and education will be needed to bring them up to date. We recommend that service managers should conduct an analysis of training needs on VSA as a matter of urgency to establish which, if any, staff need update training and education.

6.19 There are programmes of multi-disciplinary drug training being undertaken in many areas, often by drug specialists or local drug training agencies. We recommend that multi- disciplinary drugs awareness courses include adequate coverage of VSA.

6.20 Experienced professionals already possess a wide range of skills, many of which are relevant to their work with people who are misusing volatile substances. In-service education should assist them in identifying the relevant knowledge, and the generic skills can be transferred to their work with volatile substance abusers. They may also need to review their attitudes to volatile substance abusers in order to work more effectively with them.

Purchasers and providers

6.21 In a situation where services are brought in it is important to establish where responsibility for training lies. There is a danger otherwise that it will be overlooked. In setting the contract the purchaser should specify the expertise required, which might include specification of the qualifications held by staff. The provider should ensure that staff reach the appropriate level of expertise and are professionally supported to enable them to carry out the task.

National co-ordination of training on VSA

6.22 In our previous training report [(1)] we argued for a new national training development agency (paragraphs 7.8 – 7.13). This development has not taken place. There is still a gap in leadership of training at a national level and a need to identify and promote good practice in training. We recommend that the Department of Health should consider how it can support the drugs field in drawing up proposals for a co-ordinated response to the training needs of both specialists and non-specialists on VSA, in whatever capacity and however infrequently they may need to address the issue of VSA. In doing this, DH may wish to examine the possibility of assisting the Standing Conference on Drug Abuse in developing a role in co-ordinating training at a national level. There are particular needs to identify and promote good practice and also to ensure that all the relevant national validating bodies give VSA the attention which it needs in their professional education and training systems. We urge the Department of Health to consider the feasibility of this proposal.

Recommendations

1. We reiterate the need for a strong organisational base for drug education in schools, within which initial and in-service training on VSA can be provided for teachers (6.2 – 6.7)

2. The training needs on VSA for many other professions besides teachers must also be met, including those of nurses, doctors, social workers, the police, pharmacists and the probation service. We recommend that each of these professions should examine the adequacy of current training on VSA, and validating bodies should determine the basic details of knowledge on VSA appropriate to their professions. We recommend that with in-service and multidisciplinary training on drug issues, VSA should be given adequate coverage. Purchasers when setting relevant contracts should specify the degree of training on VSA which is required, and providers should ensure that it is given (6.9 - 6.21)

3. We recommend that the relevant lead bodies give their urgent attention to the issues of the substance abuse option of the level 3 Care N/SVQ containing no reference to VSA, and the lack of consideration being given within the N/SVQ systems to developing the competency of youth and community workers in relation to drug and volatile substance misusers (6.17)

4. There is still a gap in leadership of training at a national level and a need to identify and promote good practice in training. We recommend that the Department of Health should consider how it can support the drugs field in drawing up proposals for a co-ordinated response to the training needs of both specialists and non-specialists on VSA, in what ever capacity and however infrequently they may need to address the issue of VSA (6.22)

CHAPTER 7

PLANNING THE RESPONSE TO VOLATILE SUBSTANCE ABUSE

Planning the overall response to volatile substance misusers and their families at local level

7.1 There are many demands on social and health services besides those that are set by volatile substance abuse (VSA). Planning will involve:

- identifying responsibilities;
- assessing need and identifying existing resources;
- enhancing the capacity of local generic workers to deal with this problem.

Whatever the locality, the main emphasis will thus undoubtedly be on making the best of already available community resources. Where there is a high level of demand, it may sometimes be necessary to ensure that some kind of additional resource is available. Paragraphs 7.2 to 7.14 of this chapter deal with local matters while later paragraphs discuss support at national level and evaluating, nationally, the results of VSA strategies.

Identifying the lead responsibility for planning and integration of the overall local response to VSA

7.2 VSA is an issue easily lost or overlooked within so many other competing demands. We strongly believe that it is a subject which must not be allowed to slip off the agenda and our proposals here are intended to help ensure that that does not happen.

7.3 Our view is that it would not be practical to nominate a single person to be directly responsible for responding to VSA. The problems which the subject presents are manifold and the required responses cross so many different services (such as health, police, social services, education, drugs) that we believe such an arrangement would not work. And there would be a danger that if a single person was made directly responsible other services would tend to regard VSA as not their problem. Accordingly, we recommend that an individual should be made responsible for co-ordinating the local response. This would not absolve the other agencies from their duties in relation to VSA but would hopefully lead to a purposeful and integrated approach involving all those concerned.

7.4 Local arrangements for the provision of services change from time to time and vary from area to area. As a result we do not believe it would be productive for us to be prescriptive about who the co-ordinator should be; it is a matter for local decision. But identified he or she must be. In some localities it may be immediately obvious from existing structures which person should take on the role; in others less so. Where there is already a strong organisational base for responding to drug problems the response to VSA might share the same lead (provided that VSA as an issue is not then marginalised). In any event he or she will need to be clearly visible to all the key agencies and accountable to an appropriate local service. We recommend that the Director of Public Health should be responsible for ensuring that a suitable co-ordinator is identified.

7.5 The aim of the co-ordinator should be to enhance effectiveness, ensure co-ordination of effort and disseminate information. In performing that task he or she will have to assess needs and identify existing treatment, prevention and training resources and is likely to find that job easier if already involved in the local arrangements for dealing with drug misuse generally.

Assessing local need in relation to VSA

7.6 In our report "Drug Education in Schools: the Need for New Impetus" (1), published in 1993, we stressed the desirability of planning responses to drug misuse on the basis of information rather than designing the response blind to data. The present extent of need for services for VSA is in most communities today only rather poorly known. In such circumstances it would be unwise to assume that no need exists because true need has not been revealed.

7.7 In considering community-based prevention programmes and strategies, planners and providers can usefully be informed by prevention needs assessment and action enquiry. This is best focused on small geographical areas and can provide detailed and specific local background information. Where such work is undertaken on drug misuse in a locality, consideration should always be given to whether VSA should be included too.

7.8 Enquiries can explore such matters as:

- the dynamic nature of local VSA prevalence and patterns;
- public perceptions of VSA;
- prevention strategies;
- local trouble spots and environmental conditions influencing drug use patterns;
- potential responses or services required;
- media attitudes and perceptions.

Such needs assessment can also act as a stimulus to local community participation in prevention strategies. It can do this by raising awareness amongst community groups and residents, discussing local needs and problems, fostering cooperation amongst groups and agencies and initiating local action.

7.9 Ideally community action enquiries would incorporate a wide range of qualitative and quantitative methods including:

- household survey research;
- focus group discussions with local residents and young people;
- depth-interviews with local service providers and community representatives;
- interviews with a wide range of drug users;
- ethnographic field research;
- school survey research.

However such local enquiries will be restricted by available time, resources and expertise. In that case consideration should be given to obtaining as much information as possible from existing sources (for example, from talking to people who are in contact with VSA already in one capacity or another). In all events it will be better to base local plans on some information rather than none. In some cases purchasers of services might consider funding VSA research, perhaps in the context of drug misuse more generally.

Strengthening and co-ordinating services for VSA at local level

7.10 This aspect of the co-ordinating job will initially centre on finding out what relevant responses to VSA are already going on in the locality (see 7.9). Given the varied nature of the problem and of the needed responses, the trawl must be wide. Further work is likely to include review of the extent to which assessed need and service provision match up, the establishment of a co-ordinating group, and dissemination of information. Although much of this work may again be conducted within the context of overall responses to other types of substance misuse, it is also possible that local experience may, to an extent, favour a separation between VSA and other substance issues. For instance, a parents group set up to support families who have encountered problems with VSA may be happier with a separate identity rather than merging their activities with a wider response to family experience with substance problems in general. VSA will at times affect a rather younger age group than other drugs.

7.11 It would be a mistake for the person taking these co-ordinating responsibilities to try to operate as an over-burdened one-person referral point which seeks directly to meet all local VSA needs for families and users. Such an arrangement would undermine the strategy of multiple, generic, community-based capacities to deal with VSA which this chapter favours and be inconsistent with our proposals for the role of a local co-ordination which we describe in paragraphs 7.3 to 7.5.

Filling treatment gaps in the community response to VSA

7.12 Within some localities it may be that there are some needs that cannot be met by enhancing the immediate capacity of existing services or generic workers. For example, there may be no existing resource which can offer skilled and intensive help to persistent, long-term users; there may be unmet accommodation needs for the occasional user who requires residential help because of VSA; or provision of help for families may in some ways be inadequate. The role of the co-ordinator should in the longer term be that of stimulating and supporting any necessary special developments of this kind.

Setting local targets

7.13 To ensure that progress is made on strengthening the overall community response to VSA, local targets and tasks should be set. These are likely to include:-

- identification of a person with local co-ordinating responsibility for VSA and definition of their tasks;
- ensuring that the joint planning team or its equivalent has considered VSA matters;
- ensuring that local needs have been properly assessed;
- the clear identification of groups and agencies to which parents and children can go for help on VSA;

- identifying and fulfilling training needs;
- ensuring that VSA is covered in schools' syllabuses;
- ensuring relevant retailers are aware of VSA and their obligations under the law.

7.14 We should have liked to have been able to suggest suitable local outcome targets, based on repeat surveys providing local prevalence data. However the collection of such data is likely to be beyond the means of most local services. As an alternative we suggest that fulfilling the above "action points" (and there will be others which we have not identified), should be used as measures of whether the problems of VSA are being properly addressed.

Support at national level for local responses to VSA

7.15 The response to VSA which this chapter has outlined is an approach founded in the community. It has to be planned and put into operation at community level. For its success a community-based approach to treatment, prevention and training will, however, require a measure of support at the national level. Overall responsibility for national support would perhaps most appropriately lie with the Health Departments, who should consider how best they might promote the development of local action.

7.16 At national level the support for local action to secure help for users and their families might include:-

(i) means for exchanging experiences on good practice on service development, prevention and training, between those taking lead local responsibility;

(ii) central provision of training opportunities and training material (which might include distance learning material).

Evaluating the results and outcomes

7.17 It is our desire to see young lives being saved as a result of the proposals we have put forward in this report. It would therefore seem to follow that we should recommend a target based on national mortality data. In practice, however, death from VSA fluctuates greatly from year to year and for random reasons and meaningful trends cannot be identified. We therefore conclude that it would not be satisfactory to use mortality figures for setting national targets.

7.18 It is also our desire to see the prevalence of VSA reduce as a result of our proposals. However prevalence data from repeat surveys, which would be necessary to set meaningful targets, are not available and, until they are, the necessary tool for setting targets is absent. We would hope that this gap in our knowledge in prevalence will in due course be closed.

7.19 We do, however, consider it to be desirable for some sort of national measure to be in place. We suggest that periodic surveys should be carried out by the Department of Health to find out from Directors of Public Health about the local responses to VSA which have been put in place. Over time, these surveys might provide data which are useful in helping to ascertain whether coverage is adequate and to plan future responses, both nationally and locally. In the absence of the sorts of measures which we mention in paragraphs 7.17 and 7.18 we believe that such surveys would be feasible and appropriate measures.

Recommendations

1. We recommend that an effective mechanism for planning the overall response to VSA should be established throughout the country at local level (7.1 – 7.2)

2. The person who is to take lead co-ordinating responsibility for response to VSA and the office or organisation within which they are to be located

must be for local decision, but it is vital that a named person is identified, and their identity widely known in their community. We recommend that the Director of Public Health should be responsible for ensuring that a suitable co-ordinator is identified (7.3 – 7.4)

3. We recommend that plans for addressing VSA in each locality should be based on some information rather than none at all. Enquiry rather than formal research may be sufficient usefully to map the field (7.9)

4. We recommend that the local co-ordinator should identify current resources for response to VSA and related gaps in provision, establish a co-ordinating group, and disseminate information (7.10)

5. Local responses to VSA should be designed in liaison with those concerned with wider substance misuse problems (7.10 – 7.11)

6. We recommend that targets in the form of "action points" should be set at community level. Some examples are given (7.13)

7. A measure of enhanced national support will be needed. This is likely in particular to entail means for exchanging experience in good practice, and central provision of training opportunities and material. We recommend that the lead should be taken by the Health Departments and that the Departments should consider how local action can best be promoted (7.15 – 7.16)

8. We have concluded that, while it would be desirable to have national targets, the nature of the mortality data and the absence of prevalence data make the setting of these kinds of quantitative national targets impractical. However, we suggest that periodic surveys, carried out by the Department of Health, of local responses to VSA might provide data useful in helping to ascertain whether coverage is adequate and in planning future responses (7.17 – 7.19)

APPENDIX A

WORKING GROUP ON PREVENTION

Membership including co-opted members:

Professor G Edwards CBE (Chairman) – National Addiction Centre, Institute of Psychiatry, London

Mrs J Barlow – Projects Manager, Aberlour Childcare Trust, Scotland

Dr W Clee – General Medical Practitioner, Wales

Mr D Coleman – Unit Leader, Office of the Health Service Commissioner for England, London

Ms N Evans – Director, Re-Solv, Staffordshire

Dr M Farrell – Consultant Psychiatrist, Institute of Psychiatry, London

Professor D Grahame-Smith CBE – the Chairman of the Advisory Council is an ex-officio member of the Working Group

Mr R Ives – Consultant, London

Ms R Joyce – County Advisor for Drugs and Health Education, Cambridgeshire

Mr J Kay – Managing Director, Healthwise Ltd, Liverpool

Mr J Lee – Chief Executive, TACADE (the Advisory Council on Alcohol and Drug Education), Manchester

Ms C Longley – Executive Editor, Social Action, BBC Radio One, London

Ms A Marshall – Director, ADFAM National, London

Mr D Morse – Technical Manager, Shell Gas, Humberside

Mr R Odd – Head of Practice Division, Royal Pharmaceutical Society, London

Mr A Ramsay – Regional Advisor in Health Education, Scotland

Mr J Ramsey – Research Fellow, Toxicology Unit, St George's Hospital Medical School, London

Mr D Turner – formerly Director, Standing Conference on Drug Abuse, London

Mr E Unsworth – Deputy Director of Social Services, Cambridgeshire County Council

Mr P Walker – Headteacher, the Abbey School, Kent

Inspector P Wotton – Youth Affairs Branch, Metropolitan Police, London

Professor H Zeitlin – Child Psychiatrist, University College of London Medical School

Secretary:
Ms K Lidbetter (until May 1993)
Mr L Hay (May 1993 – January 1994)
Mr V Hogg (January 1994 – April 1994)
Mr R Rhodes (from April 1994)

Assistant Secretary:
Mr P Jones (until December 1991)
Mr G Lamb (December 1991 – June 1992)
Mr I Cheeseman (from June 1992)

Assisted by:

Ms S Hussein
Mr M Patel
Ms P Peddie
Miss J Woodhouse

Officials:

Home Office

Mr P Storr
Dr M Ramsay
Ms L Rogerson
Mr A Percy
Mr S Whitelegg

Department of Health

Ms C Brock
Ms C Moriarty
Mrs F Wheeler
Ms A Young

Department for Education

Mr A Thompson
Mr B Tovey
Mr P Connell

Welsh Office

Mrs K Roberts
Ms L Rolfe

Scottish Office

Mr I Snedden

Northern Ireland Office

Mr D Baker

Department of Trade and Industry

Mr J Walker

Office for Standards in Education (formerly HM Inspectorate of Schools)

Mr P Griffiths
Mr D Lewis OBE

APPENDIX B

ACKNOWLEDGEMENTS

The working group is indebted to the following individuals who gave presentations.

Mr Michael Bird, Tipp-Ex Ltd;

Dr Michael Cox and Mr David Wheeler, Bryant and May Ltd;

Dr Aneez Esmail, Mr John Ramsey and Mrs Jennifer Taylor, St George's Hospital Medical School, London;

Mr Chris Goodman, British Association of Social Workers;

Mr David Hanson and Mr Jonathan McVey, Re-Solv, Staffordshire;

Mr Richard Haydon-Knowell, Re-Solv Liaison Officer, London;

Ms Ann Higginson and Ms Shelley Hunter, Solvent Abuse Resource Group, Blackburn;

Mr Richard Ives, consultant, London; and

Mr David Roberts and Ms Sarah Ross, British Aerosol Manufacturers' Association, London.

The Working Group is also grateful for the invaluable assistance provided by Miss Mary Alison Durand, of the National Addiction Centre, London, who provided material for chapter 2 of this report, and by Mr John Ramsey, of St George's Hospital Medical School, London, who provided material for chapter 3.

APPENDIX C

BODIES AND INDIVIDUALS CONSULTED

This is a list of individuals and organisations whose views or assistance was sought by the Prevention Working Group. The Group is very grateful to all those who responded:

ACTION ON ADDICTION;
AEROSOLS INTERNATIONAL LTD;
AEROSOLS RESEARCH AND DEVELOPMENT LTD;
AKZO CHEMICALS LTD;
ASCOT MARKETING LTD;
BP CHEMICAL LTD;
BOC LTD SPECIAL GASES;
BLAGDEN INDUSTRIES PLC;
BOOTS COMPANY PLC;
BRITISH AEROSOL MANUFACTURERS' ASSOCIATION;
BRITISH ASSOCIATION OF SOCIAL WORKERS;
BRITISH EMBASSY, BOLIVIA;
BRITISH EMBASSY, BRAZIL;
BRITISH EMBASSY, COLOMBIA;
BRITISH EMBASSY, ECUADOR;
BRITISH EMBASSY, JAPAN;
BRITISH EMBASSY, MEXICO;
BRITISH EMBASSY, PARAGUAY;
BRITISH EMBASSY, VENEZUELA;
BRYANT AND MAY LTD;
CALOR GAS LTD;
CHARTERHOUSE GROUP;
CENTRE FOR DRUG RESEARCH, MALAYSIA;
COLGATE PALMOLIVE LTD;
CORONERS' SOCIETY;
COSTER AEROSOLS LTD;
CUSSONS INTERNATIONAL LTD;
DEPARTMENT OF COMMUNITY HEALTH, NEW ZEALAND;
DEPARTMENT OF THE ENVIRONMENT;
DEPARTMENT OF TRANSPORT;
DU PONT (UK) LTD;
DUNLELMAN & SON LTD;
ELIDA GIBBS;
ENFIELD BOROUGH COUNCIL;
DR ANEEZ ESMAIL;
EUROFILL UK,
EXXON CHEMICALS LTD;
GWB PRODUCTS;
GENERAL REGISTER OFFICE FOR SCOTLAND;
GENERAL REGISTER OFFICE, NORTHERN IRELAND;
PROFESSOR HAMID GHODSE;
GILLETTE (UK) LTD;
GOODMARK LTD;
DR MICHAEL GOSSOP;
GREENHILL CHEMICAL PRODUCTS LTD;
MR RICHARD HAYDON-KNOWELL;
HEALTH AND SAFETY EXECUTIVE;HM CORONER FOR MEIRIONNYDD DISTRICT OF GWYNEDD;
INSTITUTE FOR THE STUDY OF DRUG DEPENDENCE
JAMES BRIGG LTD;
JOHNSON WAX LTD;
KEEN (WORLD MARKETING) LTD;
LINDAL VALVE COMPANY LTD;
L'OREAL UK LTD;
MORGANS POMADE CO LTD;
NATIONAL ASSOCIATION OF INDEPENDENT CHILDRENS' RESOURCES;
NATIONAL ASTHMA CAMPAIGN;
NATIONAL CENTRE FOR RESEARCH INTO THE PREVENTION OF DRUG ABUSE, AUSTRALIA;
NATIONAL CHILDREN'S BUREAU;
NATIONAL COUNCIL OF VOLUNTARY CHILDCARE ORGANISATIONS;
NATIONAL FEDERATION OF RETAIL NEWSAGENTS;
NATIONAL INSTITUTE ON DRUG ABUSE, USA;
NICHOL BEAUTY PRODUCTS LTD;
NORTHERN REGIONAL DRUG AND ALCOHOL SERVICE;

OFFICE OF POPULATION CENSUSES AND SURVEYS;
PERFECT VALOIS (UK) LTD;
PRECISION VALVE (UK) LTD;
PROCTER & GAMBLE;
PUNCH SALES LTD;
RECKITT & COLMAN PRODUCTS LTD;
MR TONY REGAN;
RE-SOLV;
REVLON MANUFACTURING (UK) LTD;
RHONE-POULENC CHEMICALS LTD;
ROBERT MCBRIDE GROUP LTD;
RONSON PLC;
ROYAL COLLEGE OF GENERAL PRACTITIONERS;
ROYAL SOCIETY FOR THE PREVENTION OF ACCIDENTS;
ST GEORGE'S HOSPITAL MEDICAL SCHOOL, TOOTING;
SANMEX INTERNATIONAL PLC;
SMITHKLINE BEECHAM;
SOCIAL CARE ASSOCIATION;
SOLVENT ABUSE RESOURCE GROUP, BLACKBURN;
DR HARITH SWADI;
SWALLOWFIELD PLC;
MS JENNIFER TAYLOR;
3M UK PLC;
TIPP-EX LTD;
TRANSPORT RESEARCH LABORATORY;
UNILEVER RESEARCH;
WORLD HEALTH ORGANISATION

APPENDIX D

COMPOUNDS ASSOCIATED WITH VSA

Aliphatic hydrocarbons	acetylene n – butane (and impurities in fuel grades) isobutane hexane propane
Aromatic hydrocarbons	toluene xylene (mainly m-xylene)
Mixed hydrocarbons	petrol (gasoline)
Halogenated hydrocarbons	bromochlorodifluoromethane (BCF, CFC 1211) * carbon tetrachloride (obsolete) * chlorodifluoromethane (CFC 22) chloroform (obsolete) # dichlorodifluoromethane (CFC 12) * dichloromethane (methylene chloride) enflurane # halothane # isoflurane # methoxyflurane # monochloroethane (ethyl chloride) tetrachloroethylene 1,1,1,2-tetrafluoroethane (HFC 134a) 1,1,1-trichloroethane * trichloroethylene (obsolete as anaesthetic) # trichlorofluoromethane (CFC 11) * 1,1,2-trichlorotrifluoroethane (CFC 113) *
Oxygenated compounds	acetone butanone diethyl ether dimethyl ether ethyl acetate methyl tert-butyl ether methyl isobutyl ketone nitrous oxide #
Non-volatile hazards	lead aluminium

anaesthetics
* covered by Montreal protocol

APPENDIX E

PRODUCTS ASSOCIATED WITH VSA

Products	**Typical major volatile components**
Adhesives	
balsa wood cement contact adhesives cycle tyre repair adhesive PVC cement	ethyl acetate toluene, hexane and esters toluene and xylenes trichloroethylene
Aerosols	
air freshener deodorants, antiperspirants fly spray hair lacquer paint	purified butane, CFCs*, dimethyl ether, HCFCs purified butane, CFCs*, dimethyl ether, HCFCs purified butane, CFCs*, dimethyl ether, HCFCs purified butane, CFCs*, dimethyl ether, HCFCs purified butane, CFCs*, dimethyl ether, HCFCs
Anaesthetics	
gaseous liquid local	nitrous oxide diethyl ether, halothane, enflurane, isoflurane CFCs*, monochloroethane (ethyl chloride)
Commercial dry cleaning and degreasing	1,1,1-trichloroethane*, tetrachloroethylene, trichloroethylene
Domestic spot removers and dry cleaners	1,1,1-trichloroethane*, tetrachloroethylene, trichloroethylene
Fire extinguishers	bromochlorodifluoromethane*, CFC 11* and 12*
Fuel gases	
cigarette lighter refills butane propane	n-butane, isobutane, propane and impurities unless purified n-butane, isobutane, propane and impurities n-butane, isobutane, propane and impurities
Nail varnish/remover	acetone, esters
Paint/paint thinners	butanone, esters, hexane, toluene, xylene
Paint stripper	dichloromethane, toluene
"Typewriter" correction fluid/thinners	1,1,1-trichloroethane

* covered by Montreal Protocol

APPENDIX F

The following is a list of organisations which practitioners, parents and young people may wish to call upon for help or advice:

ADFAM National is the national charity for parents, families and friends. It runs the free National Helpline for families and provides training and support for people, projects and groups, working with the families of drug users, including parents themselves and members of family support groups. Its publication, 'Family Support Group Pack', on setting up and running groups, is available at £5.
Address: *5th Floor, Epworth House, 25 City Road, London, EC1Y 1AA. Telephone: 0171 638 3700.*

CHILDLINE is the free national helpline for children in trouble or danger. It is a 24-hour counselling service for any child or young person with any problem. Telephone: *Freephone 0800 1111.*

Daniels Publishing produces a wide range of photocopiable resource materials for health and social education.
Address: *38 Cambridge Place, Cambridge, CB2 1NS. Telephone: 01223 467144. Fax: 01223 467145.*

The **Department for Education and the Welsh Office** have produced a booklet entitled 'Drug Misuse and the Young: A Guide for the Education Service: facts for teachers, lecturers and youth workers'. It is available from: *DFE, Publications Centre, PO Box 2193, London, E15 2EU. Telephone: 0181 533 2000.*

The **Department of Health** produces a range of free leaflets, including 'Drugs and Solvents: a basic briefing', 'Drugs and Solvents: you and your child', 'Drugs: A Parent's Guide', 'Solvents: A Parent's Guide', 'Drugs and Solvents: things you should know' (for 13 to 18 year olds) and 'Drugs: a young person's guide' (for 8 to 12 year olds). Copies can be obtained from: *Health Publications Unit, Heywood Stores, No. 2 Site, Manchester Road, Heywood, Lancashire, OL10 2PZ.*

Drugline Scotland provides free confidential advice and information about drugs and solvents. It is open between 10 am and 2 am seven days a week. Telephone: 0800 776 600

The **Health Education Authority (HEA)** has one of the largest collections of health education material in the country, including information on drugs and solvents. It publishes research reports and a number of leaflets. A free catalogue is available from the publishing department. Teachers can visit and use the library by prior appointment.
Address: *Hamilton House, Mabledon Place, London, WC1H 9TX. Telephone: 0171 383 3833.*

In Scotland, health education is largely devolved to regional boards, but the **Health Education Board for Scotland** can provide contacts for different areas.
Address: *Woodburn House, Canaan Lane, Edinburgh, EH10 4SG.*

In Wales, **Health Promotion Wales** has a number of projects that include information about legal and controlled drugs.
Address: *Ffynnon-Las, Ty-Glas Avenue, Llanishen, Cardiff, CF4 5DZ. Telephone: 01222 752222.*

The **Health Information Service (HIS)** is a national freephone service available by dialling 0800 665544 from anywhere in the UK. Callers will be automatically patched through to their regional service. HIS offices are open from 10 am to 5 pm Monday to Friday. Some services are open for longer hours. Each HIS has full details of all health services including details of local services on VSA. HIS officers can also provide leaflets, information and local contacts on all drug related issues.

Healthwise is a publisher of health related educational materials with a particular focus on drugs and sex education. It has published training packs, computer programmes, books and educational card games.
Address: *9 Slater Street, Liverpool L1 4BW. Telephone: 0151 709 5505. Fax: 0151 708 9984.*

FREEPHONE Drug Problems is a 24-hour service which can put callers in touch with agencies and services providing help and advice on drug problems. Telephone: *Dial 100 and ask for 'freephone drug problems'.*

The **Home Office Central Drugs Prevention Unit** supports local drug prevention teams in a number of localities.
Address: *Horseferry House, Dean Ryle Street, London, SW1P 2AW. Telephone: 0171 217 8631.*

The **Institute for the Study of Drug Dependence (ISDD)** is a national charity concerned with the use of drugs other than tobacco and alcohol. It has many publications available on drugs and solvents. Its extensive library can be used by appointment.
Address: *Waterbridge House, 32-36 Loman Street, London, SE1 0EE. ÛTelephone: 0171 928 1211. Fax: 0171 928 7071.*

The **National Children's Bureau** operates an information project on VSA for professionals who work with young people, and it can advise on agencies operating in any part of the country. It has a research database and a list of some residential establishments prepared to admit sniffers.
Address: *The Information Officer, 8 Wakley Street, London, EC1V 7QE. Telephone: 0171 843 6000. Fax: 0171 278 9512.*

The **National Youth Agency (NYA)** is a source of information across the whole range of health education topics and publishes a wide range of material for informal educators, including 'Drugs: An Activity Pack for Youth Workers'. It has reading lists and a document loan service.
Address: *NYA, 17-23 Albion Street, Leicester, LE1 6GD. Telephone: 01162 471200. Fax: 01162 471043.*

Release offers advice, especially, on drugs and legal issues.
Address: *388 Old Street, London, EC1N 9LT. Telephone: 0171 729 9904. Emergency telephone: 0171 603 8654.*

Re-Solv, the society for the prevention of solvent and volatile substance abuse, is the national charity specialising in VSA. It produces a number of publications, including videos for professionals, retailers, parents and secondary schools. It also publishes a newsletter and a directory of relevant organisations, and produces leaflets and stickers for retailers.
Address: *30a High Street, Stone, Staffordshire, ST15 8AW. Telephone: 01785 817885. Fax: 01785 813205.*

The **Scottish Drugs Forum** is the co-ordinating body in Scotland of services for people with drug or solvent problems. It has a free publication called "Drug Problems – a Register of Helping Agencies".
Address: *5 Oswald Street, Glasgow, G1 5QR. Telephone: 0141 221 1175.*

The **St John Ambulance Association** publishes 'Emergency Aid in Schools' at around £4.00. It also has a package, 'The Three Cross Award Scheme', to help in teaching children first aid techniques; this includes a training video with support materials.
Address: *1 Grosvenor Crescent, London, SW1X 7EF. Telephone: 0171 235 5231.*

The **Standing Conference on Drug Abuse (SCODA)** is a membership organisation for organisations and individuals who work with drug-using clients. It has information on local services and on training courses.
Address: *Waterbridge House, 32-36 Loman Street, London, SE1 0EE. Telephone: 0171 928 9500. Fax: 0171 928 3343*

TACADE (the Advisory Council on Alcohol and Drugs Education) produces a wide variety of drug and health education material, and material on other aspects of personal and social education. It also provides training and is involved in project and consulting work in relation to VSA.
Address: *1 Hulme Place, The Crescent, Salford, M5 4QA. Telephone: 0161 745 8925. Fax: 0161 745 8923.*

Youth Access produces a directory of young people's counselling agencies throughout the country.
Address: *Magazine Business Centre, 11 Newarke Street, Leicester, LE1 5SS. Telephone: 01162 558 763.*

Youthlink Wales has pioneered peer-led drug education in Wales.
Address: *91a Cardiff Road, Caerphilly, CF18 1FQ.*

APPENDIX G

REFERENCES

Chapter 1

1. Prevention: Report of the Advisory Council on the Misuse of Drugs.

   HMSO Publication, 1984
   ISBN 0 11 340794 7

2. Drug Education in Schools: the Need for New Impetus. Report of the Advisory Council on the Misuse of Drugs.

   HMSO Publication, 1993
   ISBN 0 11 341081 6

3. Problem Drug Use: A Review of Training. Report of the Advisory Council on the Misuse of Drugs.

   HMSO Publication, 1990
   ISBN 0 11 340976 1

4. Drug Misuse in Britain: National Audit of Drug Misuse Statistics.

   ISDD 1991
   ISBN 0 94 883006 9

Chapter 2

1. BRY, B.H. (1983) Predicting drug abuse: review and reformulation, *The International Journal of the Addictions*, 18, pp. 223-233.

2. NEWCOMBE, M.D., MADDAHIAN, E. and BENTLER, P.M. (1986) Risk factors for drug use among adolescents: concurrent and longitudinal analyses, *American Journal of Public Health*, 76, pp. 525-531.

3. HAWKINS, J.D., CATALANO, R.F. and MILLER, J.Y. (1992) Risk and protective factors for alcohol and other drug problems in adolescence and early adulthood implications for substance abuse prevention, *Psychological Bulletin*, 112, pp. 64-105.

4. FABER, P. (1985) Solvent abuse: The East Sussex Study findings, *Education and Health*, 3, pp. 60-64.

5. ASHTON, C.H. (1990) Solvent Abuse, *British Medical Journal*, 300, pp. 135-136.

6. SOURINDHRIN, I. and BAIRD, J. (1984) Management of solvent misuse: a Glasgow community approach, *British Journal of Addiction*, 79, pp. 227-232.

7. CHADWICK, O., YULE, W. and ANDERSON, R. (1990) The examination attainments of secondary school pupils who abuse solvents, *British Journal of Educational Psychology*, 60, pp. 180-191.

8. MASTERSON, G. (1979) The management of solvent abuse, *Journal of Adolescence*, 2, pp. 65-75.

9. BIGGS, S.J., BENDER, M.P. and FOREMAN, J. (1983) Are there psychological differences between persistent solvent-abusing delinquents and delinquents who do not abuse solvents? *Journal of Adolescence*, 6, pp. 71-86.

10. GARDINER, D. and BIDDLE, D. (1985) Cracking the glue habit, *Social Work Today*, Feb 1985, pp. 18.

11. IVES, R. (1993) Drug Notes 6: Solvents (London, ISDD).

12. EDEH, J. (1989) Volatile substance abuse in relation to alcohol and illicit drugs: psychosocial perspectives, *Human Toxicology*, 8, pp. 313-317.

13. ZUR, J. and YULE, W. (1990) Chronic solvent abuse: 2. Relationship with depression, *Child: Care, Health and Development*, 16, pp. 21-34.

14. SOURINDHRIN, I. (1988) Volatile substance abuse, in: HOWELLS, J.G. (Ed.) *Modern Perspectives in Psychosocial Pathology*, pp. 89-112 (New York, Brunner Mazel Inc).

15. RICHARDSON, H. (1989) Volatile substance abuse: evaluation and treatment, *Human Toxicology*, 8, pp. 319-322.

16. TUART, P. (1986) Solvents and schoolchildren – knowledge and experimentation among a group of young people aged 11-18, *Health Education Journal*, 45, pp. 84-86.

17. COOKE, B.R.B., EVANS, D.A. and FARROW, S.C. (1988) Solvent abuse in secondary schoolchildren – a prevalence study, *Community Medicine*, 10, pp. 8-13.

18. DIAMOND, I.D., PRITCHARD, C., CHOUDRY, N., FIELDING, M., COX, M. and BUSHELL, D. (1988) The incidence of drug and solvent misuse among Southern English normal comprehensive schoolchildren, *Public Health*, 102, pp. 107-114.

19. SWADI, H. (1988) Drug and substance use among 3,333 London Adolescents, *British Journal of Addiction*, 83, pp. 935-942.

20. TAYLOR, J.C., NORMAN, C.L., BLAND, J.M., ANDERSON, H.R. and RAMSEY, J.D. (1994) Trends in deaths associated with abuse of volatile substances 1971-1992. Report No. 7 St George's Hospital Medical School, London.

21. RAMSEY, J., ANDERSON, H.R., BLOOR, K., and FLANAGAN, R.J. (1989) An introduction to the practice, prevalence and chemical toxicology of volatile substance abuse, *Human Toxicology*, 8, pp. 261-269.

22. O'CONNOR, D (1987) Glue sniffers with special needs, *British Journal of Special Education*, 14, pp. 94-97.

23. PARROTT, J. (1990) Solvent abuse, in: BLUGLASS, R. and BOWDEN, P. (Eds.) *Principles and Practice of Forensic Psychiatry*. pp. 903-911 (Edinburgh, Churchill Livingstone).

24. WATSON, J. (1986) *Solvent Abuse: The Adolescent Epidemic?* (London, Croom Helm Ltd).

25. JACOBS, A.M. and GHODSE, A.H. (1988) Delinquency and regular solvent abuse: an unfavourable combination? *British Journal of Addiction*, 83, pp. 965-968.

26. LOCKHART, W.H. & LENNOX, M. (1983) The extent of solvent abuse in a regional secure unit sample, *Journal of Adolescence*, 6, pp. 43-55.

27. EVANS, A.C. & RAISTRICK, D. (1987) Patterns of use and related harm with toluene based adhesives and butane gas, *British Journal of Psychiatry*, 150, pp. 773-776.

28. DAVIES, B., THORLEY, A. and O'CONNOR, D. (1985) Progression of addiction careers in young adult solvent misusers, *British Medical Journal*, 290, pp. 109-110.

29. PLANT, M. and PLANT, M. (1992) *Risk-Takers: Alcohol, Drugs, Sex and Youth*. (London, Routledge).

30. IVES, R. (1990) Sniffing out the solvent users. In ASHTON, M. & BALDWIN, W. (Eds.) *Drug misuse in Britain*, pp. 30-37 (London, ISDD).

31. CHADWICK, O., ANDERSON, R., BLAND, M. and RAMSEY, J. (1989) Neuropsychological consequences of volatile substance abuse: a population based study of secondary school pupils, *British Medical Journal*, 298, pp. 1679-1684.

32. BALDING, J. (1992) *Young people in 1991*. University of Exeter.

33. MOTT, J. and MIRRLEES-BLACK, C. (1993) Self-reported drug misuse in England and Wales: main findings from the 1992 British Crime Survey. Research Findings No. 7. Home Office Research and Statistics Department, London.

34. LEITNER, M., SHAPLAND, J. and WILES, P. (1993) Drugs usage and drugs prevention: The views and habits of the general public. (London, HMSO).

35. PARKER, H. and MEASHAM, F. (1994) Pick 'n' mix: changing patterns of illicit drug use amongst 1990s adolescents, *Drugs: Education, Prevention and Policy*, 1, pp. 5-13.

36. PARKER, J., POOL, Y., RAWLE, R. and GAY, M. (1988) Monitoring problem drug use in Bristol, *British Journal of Psychiatry*, 152, pp. 214-221.

37. ALLISON, W.M. & JERROM, D.W.A. (1984) Glue sniffing: a pilot study of the cognitive effects of long-term use, *International Journal of the Addictions*, 19, pp. 453-458.

38. ANDERSON, H.R., MACNAIR, R.S. and RAMSEY, J.D. (1985) Deaths from abuse of volatile substances: a national epidemiological study, *British Medical Journal*, 290, pp. 304-307.

39. SWADI, H. (1994) Psychiatric symptoms in adolescents who abuse volatile substances. In press/personal communication.

40. POTTIER, A.C.W., TAYLOR, J.C., NORMAN, C.L., MEYER, L.C., ANDERSON, H.R. and RAMSEY, J.D. (1992) Trends in deaths associated with abuse of volatile substances 1971-1990. Report No. 5 St George's Hospital Medical School, London.

41. SHEPHERD, R.T. (1989) Mechanism of sudden death associated with volatile substance abuse, *Human Toxicology*, 8, pp. 287-292.

42. WADA, K. and FUKUI, S. (1993) Prevalence of volatile substance inhalation among junior high school students in Japan and background life style of users, *Addiction*, 88, pp. 89-100.

43. CASSWELL, S. (1992) Alcohol and other recreational drug issues in New Zealand, *Journal of Drug Issues*, 22, pp. 797-805.

44. DUNN, J. (1994) Street children and volatile substance misuse – letter from Brazil, *Psychiatric Bulletin*, 18, pp. 495-496.

45. BEAUVAIS, F. (1992) Volatile solvent abuse: trends and patterns, in: SHARPE, C.W., BEAUVAIS, F. and SPENCE, R. (Eds.) *Inhalant Abuse: A Volatile Research Agenda*. NIDA Research Monograph 129. US Department of Health and Human Services, Rockville, Maryland, pp. 13-42.

Chapter 3

1. FLANAGAN, R.J., RUPRAH, M., MEREDITH, T.J. and RAMSEY, J.D. (1990) An introduction to the clinical toxicology of volatile substances, *Drug safety*, 5, pp. 359-383.

2. STREETE, P.J., RUPRAH, M., RAMSEY, J.D. and FLANAGAN, R.J. (1992) Detection and identification of volatile substances by headspace capillary gas chromatography to aid the diagnosis of acute poisoning, *Analyst*, 117, pp. 1111-1127.

3. TAKEUCHI, Y., HISANAGA, N., ONO, Y., SHIBATA, E., SAITO, I. and IWATA, M. (1993) Modification of metabolism and neurotoxicity of hexane by co-exposure of toluene, *International Archives of Occupational and Environmental Health*, 65, pp. S227-S230.

4. LOF, A., WALLEN, M. and WIGAEUS HJELM, E. (1990) Influence of paracetamol and acetylsalicylic acid on the toxicokinetics of toluene, *Pharmacology and Toxicology*, 66, pp. 138-141.

5. SATO, A. (1991) The effect of environmental factors on the pharmokinetic behaviour of organic solvent vapours, *Annals of Occupational Hygiene*, 35, pp. 525-541.

6. BAELUM, J. (1991) Human solvent exposure. Factors influencing the pharmacokinetics and acute toxicity, [review], *Pharmacology and Toxicology*, 68 Suppl 1, pp. 1-36.

7. HJELM, E.W., NASLUD, P.H. and WALLEN, M. (1988) Influence of cigarette smoking on the toxicokinetics of toluene in humans, *Journal of Toxicology and Environmental Health*, 25, pp. 155-163.

8. SHEPHERD, R.T. (1989) Mechanism of sudden death associated with volatile substance abuse, *Human toxicology*, 8, pp. 287-291.

9. LIU, J., LASTER, M.J., TAHERI, S., EGER, E.I., KOBLIN, D.D. and HALSEY, M.J. (1993) Is there a cutoff in anaesthetic potency for the normal alkanes? *Anaesthesia and Analgesia*, 77, pp. 12-18.

10. BAS, M. (1970) Sudden sniffing death, *Journal of the American Medical Association*, 212, pp. 2075-2079.

11. CLARK, D.G. and TINSTON, D.H. (1982) Acute inhalation toxicity of some halogenated and non-halogenated hydrocarbons, *Human Toxicology*, 1, pp. 239-247.

12. GUNN, J., WILSON, J. and MACKINTOSH, A.F. (1989) Butane sniffing causing ventricular fibrillation [letter], Lancet, 1, pp. 617.

13. KNISELY, J.S., REES, D.C. and BALSTER, R.L. (1990) Discriminative stimulus properties of toluene in the rat, *Neurotoxicology and Teratology*, 12, pp. 129-133.

14. BALSTER, R.L. (1987) Abuse potential evaluation of inhalants, *Drug and Alcohol Dependence*, 19, pp. 7-15.

15. EVANS, E.B. and BALSTER, R.L. (1991) CNS depressant effects of volatile organic solvents, *Neuroscience and Biobehavioral Reviews*, 15, pp. 233-241.

16. ZUR, J. and YULE, W. Chronic solvent abuse. (1990) 1. Cognitive sequelae. Child: Care, *Health and Development*, 16, pp. 1-20.

17. CHADWICK, O., ANDERSON, R., BLAND, M. and RAMSEY, J. (1989) Neuropsychological consequences of volatile substance abuse: a population based study of secondary school pupils, *British Medical Journal*, 298, pp. 1679-1683.

18. KING, M.D. (1982) Neurological sequelae of toluene abuse, *Human Toxicology*, 1, pp. 281-287.

19. WISEMAN, M.N. and BANIM, S. (1987) "Glue sniffer's" heart? *British Medical Journal – Clinical Research*, 294, pp. 737.

20. ROSENBERG, N.L. and SHARP, C.W. (1992) Solvent toxicity: A neurological focus, in: SHARP, C.W., BEAUVAIS, F. and SPENCE, R. (Eds.) *NIDA Research Monograph Series no. 129* pp. 117-171. National Institute of Health pub. no. 93-3481, Rockville, Maryland, USA.

21. GRASSO, P. (1988) Neurotoxic and neurobehavioral effects of organic solvents on the nervous system, *Occupational Medicine: State of the Art Reviews*, 3, pp. 525-539.

22. PRYOR, G., REBERT, C., KASSAY, K., KUIPER, H. and GORDON, R. (1991) The hearing loss associated with exposure to toluene is not caused by a metabolite, *Brain Research Bulletin*, 27, pp. 109-113.

23. HOLLO, G. and VARGA, M. (1992) Toluene and visual loss [letter; comment], *Neurology*, 42, pp. 266.

24. LOLIN, Y. (1989) Chronic neurological toxicity associated with exposure to volatile substances, *Human Toxicology*, 8, pp. 293-300.

25. UNGVARY, G., TATRAI, E., SZEBERENYI, S., RODICS, K., LORINCZ, M. and BARCZA, G. (1982) Effect of toluene exposure on the liver under different experimental conditions, *Experimental and Molecular Pathology*, 36, pp. 347-360.

26. LINDEMANN, R. (1991) Congenital renal tubular dysfunction associated with maternal sniffing or organic solvents, *Acta Paediatrica Scandinavica*, 80, pp. 882-884.

27. SHAFER, N. and SHAFER, R. (1982) Tetrachloroethylene: a cause of permanent kidney damage, *Medical Trial Technique Quarterly*, 28, pp. 387-295.

28. GUPTA, R.K., VAN DER MEULEN, J. and JOHNY, K.V. (1991) Oliguric acute renal failure due to glue-sniffing. Case report, *Scandinavian Journal of Urology and Nephrology*, 25, pp. 247-250.

29. TUNEK, A., HOGSTEDT, B. and OLOFSSON, T. (1982) Mechanism of benzene toxicity. Effects of benzene and benzene metabolites on bone marrow cellularity, number of granulopoietic stem cells and frequency of micronuclei in mice, *Chemico-Biological Interactions*, 39, pp. 129-138.

30. HERSH, J.H. (1989) Toluene embryopathy: two new cases, *Journal of Medical Genetics*, 26, pp. 333-337.

31. WILKINS HAUG, L. and GABOW, P.A. (1991) Toluene abuse during pregnancy: Obstetric complications and perinatal outcomes, *Obstetrics and Gynaecology*, 77, pp. 504-509.

32. DONALD, J.M., HOOPER, K. and HOPENHAYN RICH, C. (1991) Reproductive and developmental toxicity of toluene: a review. *Environmental Health Perspectives*, 94, pp. 237-244.

33. CRONK, S.L., BARKLEY, D.E. and FARRELL, M.F. (1985) Respiratory arrest after solvent abuse, *British Medical Journal – Clinical Research*, 290, pp. 897-898.

34. IKEDA, M. and, TSUKAGOSHI, H. (1990) Encephalopathy due to toluene sniffing. Report of a case with magnetic resonance imaging, *European Neurology*, 30, pp. 347-349.

35. SMITH, M.S. (1990) The neurological sequelae to toluene inhalation, *Journal of the Royal Naval Medical Service*, 76, pp. 69-74.

36. BYRNE, A., KIRBY, B., ZIBIN, T. and ENSMINGER, S. (1991) Psychiatric and neurological effects of chronic solvent abuse, *Canadian Journal of Psychiatry*, 36, pp. 735-738.

37. SCHIKLER, K.N., SEITZ, K., RICE, J.F. and STRADER, T. (1982) Solvent abuse associated cortical atrophy, *Journal of Adolescent Health Care*, 3, pp. 37-39.

38. EHYAI, A. and FREEMON, F.R. (1983) Progressive optic neuropathy and sensorineural hearing loss due to chronic glue sniffing, *Journal of Neurology, Neurosurgery & Psychiatry*, 46, pp. 349-351.

39. SPOONER, R.J., BIRRELL, R.C., MCLELLAND, A.S., BAIRD, J.A. and SOURINDHRIN, I. (1984) Observed activities of serum creatine kinase: total and B subunit activity and other enzymes in young persons abusing solvents, *Journal of Clinical Pathology*, 37, pp. 455-459.

40. BOSCH, X., CAMPISTOL, J.M., MONTOLIU, J. and RVERT, L. (1988) Myelofibrosis and focal segmental glomerulosclerosis associated with toluene poisoning, *Human Toxicology*, 7, pp. 357-361.

41. BROWN, J.H., HADDEN, D.R. and HADDEN, D.S. (1991) Solvent abuse, toluene acidosis and diabetic ketoacidosis, *Archives of Emergency Medicine*, 8, pp. 65-67.

42. SCHIKLER, K.N., LANE, E.E., SEITZ, K. and COLLINS, W.M. (1984) Solvent abuse associated pulmonary abnormalities, *Advances in Alcohol & Substance Abuse*, 3, pp. 75-81.

43. CLAYDON, S.M. (1988) Myocardial degeneration in chronic solvent abuse, *Medicine, Science & the Law*, 28, pp. 217-218.

44. CUNNINGHAM, S.R., DALZELL, G.W., MCGIRR, P. and KHAN, M.M. (1987) Myocardial infarction and primary ventricular fibrillation after glue sniffing, *British Medical Journal* – Clinical Research, 294, pp. 737-740.

45. SUZUKI, T., KASHIMURA, S. and UMETSU, K. (1983) Thinner abuse and aspermia, *Medicine, Science & the Law*, 23, pp. 199-202.

46. SALAMANCA-G"MEZ, F., HERNANDEZ, S., PALMA, V. ET AL. (1989) Chromosome abnormalities and sister chromatid exchanges in children with acute intoxication due to inhalation of volatile substances, *Archives of Environmental Health*, 44, pp. 49-53.

47. SIEGEL, E. and WASON, S. (1992) Sudden sniffing death following inhalation of butane and propane: changing trends, in: SHARP, C.N., BEAUVAIS, F. and SPENCE, R. (Eds.) *NIDA Research Monograph Series*, pp. 193-201. National Institute of Health pub. no. 93-3481, Rockville, Maryland, USA.

48. ROBERTS, M.J., MCIVOR, R.A. and ADGEY, A.A. (1990) Asystole following butane gas inhalation, *British Journal of Hospital Medicine*, 44, pp. 294.

49. ELLIOTT, D.C. (1991) Frostbite of the mouth: a case report, *Military Medicine*, 156, pp. 18-19.

50. GRAY, M.Y. and LAZARUS, J.H. (1993) Butane inhalation and hemiparesis, *Journal of Toxicology – Clinical Toxicology*, 31, pp. 483-485.

51. OTT, M.G. (1990) Assessment of 1,3-butadiene epidemiology studies, *Environmental Health Perspectives*, 86, pp. 135-141.

52. MCLEOD, A.A., MARJOT, R., MONAGHAN, M.J., HUGH-JONES, P. and JACKSON, G. (1987) Chronic cardiac toxicity after inhalation of 1,1,1- trichloroethane, *British Medical Journal* – Clinical Research, 294, pp. 727-729.

53. BROWN, D.P. and KAPLAN, S.D. (1987) Retrospective cohort mortality study of dry cleaner workers using perchloroethylene, *Journal of Occupational Medicine*, 29, pp. 535-541.

54. CAMPOS OUTCALT, D. (1992) Trichloroethylene: environmental and occupational exposure, *American Family Physician*, 46, pp. 495-500.

55. HALL, D.M.B., RAMSEY, J., SCHARTZ, M.S. and DOOKUN, D. (1986) Neuropathy in a petrol sniffer, *Archives of Disease in Childhood*, 61, pp. 900-916.

56. ROSS, C.A. (1982) Gasoline sniffing and lead encephalopathy, *Canadian Medical Association Journal*, 127, pp. 1195-1197.

Chapter 4

1. Drug Education in Schools: the Need for New Impetus: Report of the Advisory Council on the Misuse of Drugs.

   HMSO Publication 1993
   ISBN 0 11 341081 6

2. Solvents – A Parent's Guide

   HMSO Publication 1992
   HSSH J1462NJ

3. Drugs and Solvents – you and your child

   HMSO Publication 1993
   HSSH J09-1517NJ

4. Drugs and Solvents – things you should know

   HMSO Publication 1994
   HSSH J03-2627RP

5. Drugs and Solvents – a young person's guide

   HMSO Publication 1993
   HSSH J11-1770NJ

6. Drug and Solvent Misuse – a basic briefing

   Department of Health Publication

7. TAYLOR, J.C., NORMAN, C.L., BLAND, J.M., ANDERSON, H.R. and RAMSEY, J.D. (1994) Trends in deaths associated with abuse of volatile substances 1971-1992. Report No. 7 St George's Hospital Medical School, London

Chapter 6

1. Problem Drug Use: A Review of Training. Report of the Advisory Council on the Misuse of Drugs.

   HMSO Publication, 1990
   ISBN 0 11 340976 1

2. Drug Education in Schools: the Need for New Impetus. Report of the Advisory Council on the Misuse of Drugs.

   HMSO Publication, 1993
   ISBN 0 11 341081 6

Chapter 7

1. Drug Education in Schools: the Need for New Impetus. Report of the Advisory Council on the Misuse of Drugs.

   HMSO Publication, 1993
   ISBN 0 11 341081 6

INDEX

A

B

C

D

E

F

G

H

I

J

L

M

N

O

P

R

S

T

U

V

W

Y

Printed in the United Kingdom for HMSO
Dd.300346, C20, 4/95, 3400, 5673, 321294